GILES'S
LABORATORY COURSE IN DYEING
(FOURTH EDITION)

Giles's
Laboratory course
in dyeing *Fourth edition*

by David G Duff and Roy S Sinclair

Department of Chemistry, Paisley College of Technology, Paisley, Scotland

Society of Dyers and Colourists

Published by the Society of Dyers and Colourists, PO Box 244, Perkin House, 82 Grattan Road, Bradford, West Yorkshire BD1 2JB, England, on behalf of the Dyers' Company Publications Trust.

Typeset by the Society of Dyers and Colourists and printed by Staples Printers Rochester Ltd

ISBN 0 901956 49 X

Dyers' Company Publications Trust

The Dyers' Company Publications Trust was instituted by the Worshipful Company of Dyers of the City of London in 1971 to encourage the publication of textbooks and other aids to learning in the science and technology of colour and coloration and related fields. The Society of Dyers and Colourists acts as trustee for the fund, its Textbooks Committee acting as the Trust's technical subcommittee.

Preface to the Fourth Edition

Though the format of this edition differs somewhat from the previous ones, its aim remains the same, namely that it should 'act as a guide to instruction in the principles of dyeing' for students at stages up to first degree level.

Shortly before his death, Professor Giles discussed with us his ideas for a new edition. It was decided to undertake a major revision by deleting outdated methods and concentrating on well established ones, taking account of present day practice. We also undertook the task of checking the results of every experiment considered for inclusion in this edition and for help with this we gratefully acknowledge the assistance provided by a grant from the Manpower Services Commission under the Community Programme scheme. This allowed us to employ a small team at Paisley College, part of whose remit was the development of the experiments included here. We have retained all their sample dyeings and trust that the attempts of others to follow the experimental instructions will give results as successful as theirs.

The changed format agreed with Professor Giles split the theoretical aspects of dyeing into the introductory material of Part I and the more advanced theory placed in Part III. The main section of the manual remains essentially unchanged in style, except that a Results section has been included, and it is hoped that students may better understand the principles by being asked to explain 'why' in addition to 'how'. Some of the questions asked in the experiments are directed to those studying for ASDC or who are in the final year of a degree course and such students are encouraged to consult relevant literature sources.

The bibliography and references quoted in this edition have been restricted to the more important textbooks and journals likely to be readily available in laboratories concerned with training in dyeing techniques.

Readers should note that, although all the dyestuffs mentioned in the book are thought to be non-toxic, this does not mean that they are non-hazardous in all circumstances. If they are treated with the respect that should be accorded to most laboratory chemicals they should pose no significant risk to students. All dyestuffs and other chemicals need to be treated with care to avoid inhalation, ingestion, and skin and eye contact. In three specific cases (C.I. Disperse Red 1, C.I. Disperse Red 11 and C.I. Disperse Yellow 3) there is evidence that there is a possibility of allergic skin reaction, and special precautions are needed to avoid exposure.

Finally it has been a privilege for both of us to have been associated with Professor Giles in the preparation of the recent editions of this manual, and although he was only in at the start of this one, we trust he would have been satisfied with the end result. He was after all a man of principles – in every sense.

DAVID G DUFF
ROY S SINCLAIR

Contents

PART III – BACKGROUND THEORY

PART I

General principles

1 INTRODUCTION

This manual is designed as an introduction to the techniques used in the dyeing of textile materials. Emphasis is placed on the illustration of those factors which are of importance in commercial dyeing, although it is not always possible to simulate conditions used in certain types of specialised commercial dyeing machinery. Most of the experiments are in fact designed to be carried out with the simplest of equipment, although some advanced experiments are included utilising pH meters, spectrophotometers, colour measuring equipment, etc. Also included are some basic experiments using natural dyes.

The process of dyeing involves the application of dyes to a desired textile in such a way that a previously defined coloured textile is obtained, with properties that are satisfactory for the end use. Any study of dyeing requires therefore:

(a)   An appreciation of the nature of textile materials and of dyes
(b)   A knowledge of the basic factors controlling the uptake of dyes from the dyebath
(c)   Assessment of the colour and the other relevant properties of dyed textile materials.

As indicated in the preface to this edition, the manual is organised in three parts, i.e.:
Part I – General principles
Part II – Practical experiments
Part III – Background theory.

This arrangement was chosen so that, in reading Part I prior to carrying out the experimental work, students are made aware of the basic facts about the materials they are handling and the practices of laboratory dyeing, and some guide is given as to the assessment of the results. Part II gives the experimental instructions under the headings 'Procedure' and 'Results'. In Part III the background theory to the experimental topics is covered in a concise way, to provide the student with a better insight into the theories and methods of dyeing. A knowledge of the background theory in Part III is essential for students tackling the more advanced experiments described at the end of Part II.

However, all students are encouraged to read that section of Part III that is appropriate to the experiment being carried out and to consult the references listed.

1.1 NATURE OF TEXTILE MATERIALS

Textile materials can take the form of loose fibres, spun and filament yarns, or woven and knitted materials. Although the precise form of the material may define the type of machinery best used on a commercial scale, it is the nature of the fibre itself that determines the class of dye and usually the dyeing process to be used.

For convenience in studying their dyeing properties, fibres may be broadly divided into the following classes:

(a)   *Cellulosic* – cotton, linen, jute, viscose, etc. These are all derived from vegetable sources and are composed principally of cellulose, the structural material of plants

(b) *Protein* – wool, silk and hair fibres are animal proteins
(c) *Cellulose acetates* – the cellulose acetate fibres (di- and tri-acetate) are manufactured from cellulose raw material
(d) *Synthetic polymer fibres* – nylons, acrylics (Orlon, Courtelle, Acrilan) and polyesters (Terylene, Dacron, Crimplene, etc.).

1.2 NATURE OF DYES

Dyes are very highly coloured organic chemicals synthesised from products of the petro-chemical and coal-tar industries. Dyeing is invariably carried out in an aqueous medium and hence most dyes are supplied in water-soluble form. Certain dyes, such as vat dyes, have to be converted to a soluble form before dyeing, whilst others such as disperse dyes are used in the form of very fine dispersions, though these, with the aid of added surfactants, are appreciably soluble in water at the temperatures used in dyeing.

Dyes are divided into classes by the dyer according to their ability to dye various fibres but the dye chemist has a different method of classification, based on the dye's chemical structure. The main classes, as arranged by the dyer, may be illustrated by Table 1.1, in which they are shown according to the fibres on which they are used.

TABLE 1.1

Classification of dyes according to the principal fibre classes

Cellulosic	Protein	Cellulose acetates	Nylon	Acrylic	Polyester
Direct	Acid (including	Disperse	Disperse	Basic	Disperse
Sulphur	metal-complex)		Acid (including	Acid	
Azoic	Mordant		metal-complex)		
Vat	Reactive		Mordant		
Reactive					

In the present text dyes are defined in terms of their *Colour Index* [1] classification. This work lists almost all the dyes now in use, giving their fastness properties, uses, hues and in many cases the chemical constitution of the essential colorant they contain.

Some dyes are given two *Colour Index* reference numbers, e.g. C.I. Acid Red 1; C.I. 18050. The first number (the C.I. generic name) refers to the section of the *Colour Index* describing the technical properties of the dye and the second number (the C.I. constitution number) refers to the section giving the chemical constitution and the method of manufacture, in cases where this information has been disclosed. Under the C.I. generic name will be found a list of all the different trade names under which any given dye is sold by different manufacturers. The student should be encouraged to study all the information in the *Colour Index* about each dye he or she has used.

Colouring matters which are applied to any material in the form of insoluble particles are known as pigments. Pigments are of importance in textile printing when they are bound to the fabric by a resin.

1.3 CHOICE OF DYES

One reason for the large number of commercial dyes available is that any dyed textile material may have to withstand one or more of a wide range of processes of manufacture and later be subjected to a variety of different types of wear and tear in use.

The correct choice of dye for any given circumstance requires considerable knowledge and experience, and nothing more than a bare outline of the underlying principles can be given here. A few typical examples, selected at random, of some of the factors to be considered in dye selection are given below.

Nature of wear and tear in use

Many textiles must withstand severe exposure to sunlight or to repeated washing. Thus curtains and fabrics for outer garments must be fast to light, and fabrics for awnings and deckchairs must withstand sunlight and also rain; knitted wool goods should be fast to washing; cotton shirting and handkerchiefs must withstand hot washing conditions, and so on. Dyes chosen for a specific application must therefore take account of the requirements of that application.

Nature of the manufacturing process

Cotton goods having coloured threads on a white ground may have to be subjected to boiling with alkali under pressure (kier boiling) and bleaching subsequent to weaving. The type of wool textile known as tweed at one stage in its manufacture has to undergo a vigorous mechanical treatment in the presence of soap or sometimes an acid solution, known as milling; this is liable to cause bleeding of colour unless 'fast-to-milling' dyes are used.

Nature of the dyeing process employed

Apart from the above treatments to which the dyed materials are subjected, the nature of the dyeing process itself is important in determining the correct choice of dye class. Thus for fabric dyed in the piece only the most level-dyeing dyes can be used, because the slightest inequality in colour in a different area of the fabric would spoil the appearance of the goods. If loose fibre is being dyed, however, levelness is of less importance, because any portions of uneven appearance in the dyed mass will be evenly distributed when the fibre is subsequently converted into yarn; less level-dyeing but faster dyes can therefore be chosen in this case. If the type of dyeing machine used is one into which the dye liquor is pumped through a container packed tightly with loose fibre, or through a cake or cheese of yarn, then it is important for the dye to be in true solution or maintained as a fine stable dispersion during the dyeing process. If the dye were merely suspended as coarse particles in the liquor, these would be filtered out during the passage of the liquor through the fibres, and the layers that the liquor first reached would be more heavily dyed than the rest.

These are some of the considerations underlying the choice of dyes in practice. Other factors such as cost and colour value may occur to the student as he or she becomes more familiar with the behaviour of dyes when carrying out the laboratory experiments. The significance of commercial factors and discussions of dye selection will be found in the SDC (Dyers' Company) textbooks mentioned throughout this book.

Commercial dyes used in the experiments

Almost all the dyes used in the experiments in this book are designated by their C.I. generic name and it can be assumed, unless otherwise stated, that these refer to standard brands (100 or 100%). Commercial dyes are marketed as mixtures with a colourless diluent such as common salt or sodium sulphate, which serves as a means of controlling their strength in manufacture, and for brands of increased dye strength (e.g. 150 or 250%), dye recipes should be adjusted accordingly.

New ranges of dyes and auxiliaries are often introduced and established ones withdrawn, leading to frequent deletions from the *Colour Index*, and this creates difficulties in preparing detailed experiments such as those described in the following chapters. To complicate this situation further, there are frequent changes of product names by the dye manufacturers. The availability of any given product mentioned in this book therefore cannot always be assumed. We have, however, made every effort to ensure that the information was correct at the time of the experimental trials and of writing. Students wishing to learn more about commercial nomenclature of dyes should refer to the *Colour Index* and other published works [2].

1.4 SOME TECHNICAL TERMS USED IN DYEING (see also Appendix A)
The process of transfer of dye from the dyebath to the fibre is known technically as *exhaustion*. The amount of dye finally transferred to the fibre is often expressed quantitatively as a percentage of the dye originally present in the liquor, *100% exhaustion* meaning, of course, that no dye is left in the bath.

The property known as *levelness* is essential in a dyed yarn or fibre. A dyeing is level (a) when it is of the same depth all over the textile material and (b) when it shows complete *penetration* of the material, i.e. when the fibre or yarns, if pulled apart, show no lighter portions inside. Both these properties are ensured by careful attention to technique, e.g. by using good agitation, by control of the rate of dyeing so that it is not too rapid, and by allowing sufficient time in the bath. One type of unlevelness, which applies more particularly to dyeing wool, is *skitteriness,* a term used to describe the variation in depth of colour that occurs between individual fibres. It can occur even between different parts of the same fibre, particularly between the lower or root portion of a wool fibre and the outer end or tip, which, having received more exposure to the atmosphere and sunlight, has become chemically degraded. The tip is more readily dyed than is the rest of the wool fibre. Skitteriness gives a 'pepper-and-salt' appearance to a dyed fabric, and cannot be so readily avoided as other forms of unlevelness, since it is also dependent on the nature of the dye itself. New dyeing assistants have been developed to eliminate skitteriness.

The initial rate at which the dye exhausts is referred to as its *strike*, while the transfer of dye from a heavily dyed to lightly dyed or undyed portion of the same material during impregnation–fixation dyeing processes is referred to as *migration*. A gradual change in depth or hue along the length of dyed fabric is known as *ending* or *tailing*.

The term *matching to shade* refers to the use of dye mixtures to obtain an exact match to the colour of a given pattern; when this match is achieved the material is said to be *on shade.*

Chemicals which are added to a dyebath to prevent dye from being taken up by one of the fibres in a mixture, and which act by being preferentially adsorbed themselves on that fibre, are usually known as *reserving agents* or *blocking agents.*

Stripping is the process of removing partially or completely unwanted dye from a fibre. A list of definitions of some terms used in textile processing is given in Appendix A.

REFERENCES
1.   'Colour Index International' (Bradford: SDC/AATCC, 1971, 1982, 1987).
2.   C L Bird, J.S.D.C., **61** (1945) 321.

2 PRACTICAL CONSIDERATIONS

The essential requirements of a dyed material are that it should be of correct colour with a good degree of levelness and complete penetration of the dye to the inner portions of each fibre, combined with the achievement of a predetermined level of fastness. These qualities, as already mentioned, are the result partly of choice of dye, and partly of care and attention to detail in the dyeing procedure. Thus, for example, too rapid a rise in temperature of the dyebath and insufficient agitation of the material are very liable to cause unlevel dyeing. This can often occur on the laboratory scale by placing the dyeing vessel on a heated hotplate. Proper preparation of the material before dyeing is also a prerequisite for uniform dyeing.

2.1 APPARATUS AND MATERIALS

All the dyeing tests in this manual are designed to be made with simple apparatus, but several of the analytical experiments are preferably performed with the use of more specialised equipment, e.g. a pH meter and a spectrophotometer. A tristimulus colorimeter or reflectance spectrophotometer will be necessary for the experiments on colour measurement. When such specialised apparatus is not available, simpler methods of recording the data may be used e.g. indicator papers for pH measurement, visual assessment of dye uptake or colour values.

The dyeing experiments are designed for use with about 5 g of textile material, so that they may be performed in small beakers; tall straight-sided vessels of about 500 ml capacity are best. The beakers may be made of porcelain, earthenware or heat-resisting glass. They may be heated on ordinary water-baths if temperatures below 95°C are required; for experiments carried out at or near the boil (100°C) electrically heated or gas-fired hotplates should be employed. For experiments above 100°C a domestic pressure cooker is suitable, if a specially designed machine is not available.

The preferred material for stirring is a Tufnol rod, which is almost unbreakable, slightly flexible and a poor conductor of heat; it is much superior in these respects to glass or metal rods. A thermometer must be used in each set of beakers, and for safety this should be enclosed in one of the perforated sheaths marketed by the laboratory-furnishing houses.

Automatically controlled machines for small-scale laboratory dyeing experiments are marketed by Goodbrand Jeffreys Ltd, Rochdale, Lancashire, and Roaches Engineering Ltd, Leek, Staffordshire, and such machines have special material holders which ensure uniform treatment during dyeing. Where fabrics require to be padded, good results can be obtained by impregnation in a large photographic developing dish, followed by squeezing on a sheet of plate glass with a rubber squeegee or a Pyrex domestic rolling pin. Small-scale padding units are manufactured by E Benz of Switzerland.

Ideally, distilled or softened water should be used in all dyeing experiments, but mains water is usually satisfactory if it is nearly neutral in reaction (pH 7) and if it has a low degree of hardness, which is the case in many towns in textile districts. Where a dye testing laboratory is attached to a dyehouse the same water should be used in both places.

Dissolved iron in water may alter the colour of some dyeings of acid and mordant dyes, and textbooks on dyeing should be consulted for a full discussion of the effects of impurities in water.

The fibres may be used in the loose state or more commonly as yarn or fabric. Fabric patterns are most easily mounted neatly on cards for reference, and the degree of levelness of the dyeing is usually more apparent on fabric than on loose fibres or yarn.

For the experiments on mixed fibres the most suitable material is knitted fabric in which yarns of the two fibres are used to form alternate bars about 1 cm wide. When these are dyed, even the smallest difference in colour between the two fibres is immediately apparent. The fabric should be knitted on a flat-rib machine, and the bars of the two yarns should be noticeably different in width or of noticeably different dimensions, so that they may be readily identified in the dyed pattern.

For some purposes it is convenient to dye film rather than fibre. Several of the materials used in synthetic-polymer fibres are also available in the form of continuous thin film, usually of 2.5 or 5.0 μm thickness. Cellophane (the non-waterproofed type should be used) is composed of the same substance as viscose fibre, whilst Melinex is the same material as polyester fibre. These materials can be readily dyed using the processes for the corresponding fibre.

Dye and reagent solutions
Except where otherwise stated, weigh 0.5 g of dry dye powder, place it in a dish or beaker, add a little cold water, paste-up well and bring the total volume up to 250 ml. Heat this to the boil, boil for a few minutes and cool before making up to the final volume (500 ml). This gives a solution strength of 1 g/l (0.1%), which is a suitable concentration for most stock solutions required in the experiments in Part II. To avoid confusion, in most cases in this manual the quantities of reagent used, e.g. acetic acid or caustic soda, refer to the undiluted substance and not to any of the various strengths of solution or 'liquors' usually employed commercially.

Preparation of the material
It is best to use scoured and bleached[1] material for all dyeing experiments, and a note should be taken of the yarn or weave specification. With such prepared material all that is necessary before dyeing is to weigh out the amount of the textile samples to be used (to within, say, 2% accuracy) and to pre-wet the material by immersion in water at, say, 50°C, before squeezing, loading into the material holder and entering into the dyebath at the required temperature.

Where the material is known to contain spinning oils, e.g. wool yarn and certain synthetic fibres, a warm (approx. 50°C) solution of synthetic detergent should be used for the pre-scour, followed by thorough rinsing in water at 50°C.

If the material has size, starch or other impurities present, special methods of preparation (e.g. enzyme desizing) have to be used; details will be found in appropriate texts.

Note that redyeing of many coloured or even white goods may be made impossible by the use of special polymer finishes (e.g. crease-resistant, showerproofing, etc.), which confer these special properties to many items of clothing.

---

1. Most synthetic fibres do not require bleaching.

Preparation of the dyebath

In the dyeing industry quantities of dyes, assistants, etc. are usually based on the weight of textile being processed (often now abbreviated to o.w.f., i.e. on weight of fibre). Thus a '2% dyeing' refers to the use of 2 g of dye per 100 g of textile material (or 2 lb per 100 lb, etc.). The volume of liquor employed (sometimes called the liquor ratio or liquor-to-goods ratio) is also given as a multiple of fibre weight. Thus, for example, a '50:1' or a '50-volume' liquor for dyeing 100 g of textile material entails the use of 5 kg (5 l) of water[1]. To calculate the quantities to be used in any experiment Eqn 2.1 may be used:

$$\text{No. of ml stock solution required} = \frac{WP}{C} \qquad (2.1)$$

where W = weight of sample to be dyed, g
$\qquad P$ = amount of dye or assistant to be used, % o.w.f.
$\qquad C$ = concentration of stock solution, %.

Thus, for example, if 5 g of wool is to be dyed to a 2% depth and the stock solution contains 1 g of dye in 250 ml (i.e. 0.4% concentration), the volume of dye solution is $(5 \times 2) \div 0.4 = 25$ ml.

Similarly, if 2% sulphuric acid and 10% Glauber's salt are to be used as assistants, and the concentrations of these substances in the stock solutions used are 1% and 10% respectively, the quantities required are 10 ml sulphuric acid solution and 5 ml Glauber's salt solution. If the liquor ratio is to be 50:1 the bath must be made up to a total volume of 250 ml.

In a few cases the quantities of assistants quoted are based on the volume of the bath instead of on the weight of the fibre. In these instances, which are very clearly differentiated in the text, the calculations present no difficulty.

A glance at the *Colour Index* will show that very many dyes are made by a number of different manufacturers, and often under different trade names. The actual depth of dyeing obtained with a dye of a given identity may vary according to the standard strength set for it by the manufacturer. However, a manufacturer may sell a dye at more than one strength. It is important therefore to record the full and exact commercial name given to the dye, including all accompanying marks, as well as its percentage depth. Amendments to manufacturers' ranges may mean that some of the dyes recommended for the experiments in Part II are no longer available. However, the experiments can be carried out successfully using alternative types of a similar nature.

2.2 THE DYEING OPERATION

The pattern must be very well agitated during the whole period of dyeing. It should be gently opened out and turned so as to expose fresh surfaces to the liquor and must not be

---

1. In laboratory practice, large ratios, say up to 100:1, are most convenient to use, because the pattern can most easily be manipulated in the large volume of water. Manipulation becomes increasingly difficult, and thus levelness may suffer, with reduction in liquor ratio, and it is hardly practicable to use ratios below 10:1 except with specially constructed apparatus. The advantage of a 'short' liquor in practice is that it usually ensures more efficient use of dyes and assistants. In the present manual a liquor ratio of 50:1 is adopted as standard in many cases. This may be varied to suit the individual apparatus in use.

allowed to rotate in a crumpled mass. A slow rise in temperature favours level dyeing with most dyes. The volume of the dyebath should be kept constant by additions of small amounts of hot water during dyeing. When additions of assistants or dye to the bath are made during dyeing, the pattern is removed from the liquor to minimise unlevel patches. When the dyeing is complete the pattern is removed, well rinsed (preferably in warm water, unless other instructions are given) and dried in hot air. Patterns can subsequently be ironed and trimmed for presentation. In a number of experiments the rate of dye uptake needs to be examined. This can be done either by (a) removing portions of the material at regular intervals or (b) measuring the percentage exhaustion of the dyebath by suitable means.

Method (a) requires the dyed samples to be dried and the amount of dye adsorbed estimated visually or by some instrumental method. An appropriate aliquot of the dyebath should be removed to keep the liquor ratio constant.

Method (b) usually involves removing an aliquot of the dyebath, suitably diluting it in a standard flask, and measuring the absorbance of the resulting dye solution using a spectrophotometer.

2.3 COLOUR AND FASTNESS ASSESSMENT

The results of dyeing experiments have been assessed traditionally by visual examination. However, in recent years instrumental assessments have been used increasingly and in some of the more advanced experiments instrumental colour measurement and assessment are examined. The results of fastness tests are also assessed visually, although quantification of the assessments is aided by the use of a series of blue wool standards (1 to 8) for light fastness , and two series of grey scales (1 to 5) for assessing either the change of colour or the degree of staining in all other fastness tests.

The wash fastness tests employed in the experimental section are the ISO tests, though the related C0 tests are now increasingly used. Thus in the experiment on the wash fastness of acid dyes on wool (section 3.3) the ISO 2, ISO 3 and domestic washing tests can be replaced by C02, C03 and C06/2 tests respectively.

Assessing the colour (visual colour matching)

In commercial dyeing operations it is usual to have the desired colour specified by a physical standard which can take any form from an artist's drawing or a few threads of material to a sliver of plastic or paint. Ideally the standard should be of the same form as the material to be dyed and be of adequate size.

In visual colour matching or colour assessment the sample and standard should be compared side by side in a suitable light. Traditionally daylight from a north-facing window was used, but this can be very variable. Hence nowadays much use is made of colour matching cabinets fitted with a selection of lamps to provide reproducible lighting conditions for colour matching at any time during the working day (or night). The lamps commonly installed include artificial daylight (illuminant D_{65}) (which should conform to BS 950 or its international equivalent), a tungsten light souce (approximating to illuminant A) and some type of fluorescent lamp (such as the triphosphor type TL84).

It is important to recognise that the quality of a colour match may depend on the viewing conditions and on the colour vision characteristics of the observer. This is particularly the case when the standard and the sample are not dyed with the same dyes or are not of the same materials. In such a situation the quality of the colour match will change when the illuminant is varied (e.g. a change from tungsten to daylight lamps). This characteristic of pairs of coloured samples arises from subtle differences in the reflection of light across the visible spectrum and is termed *metamerism* (sections 3.6 and 12.5). When metamerism is present one can expect differences of opinion among observers about the quality of a colour match.

In Part II (Experimental) there are only a few experiments where close colour matching is involved, but in many experiments assessment and description of colour differences or colour changes are required. There are many ways of describing colour change but in the textile dyeing industry it is normal practice to indicate differences in the three variables hue, strength and brightness. Thus in comparing two blue samples a colour difference may be described as:

(a)   Redder or greener (hue variable)
(b)   Fuller or thinner (strength variable)
(c)   Brighter or flatter (brightness variable).

Such differences may also be qualified by the magnitude terms 'trace', 'slight', 'little' and 'much' as measures of the size of the colour change or difference (section 12.4).

Instrumental colour measurements and assessments

Although results of dyeing experiments are best illustrated by mounting the specimens as part of the report on the experiment, it is sometimes desirable to measure and quantify the colour and colour difference (if any) using modern instrumental techniques. Certainly the preparation of dye recipes has been revolutionised by the advent of computer colour matching (sections 8.10 and 12.6).

Colour measurement techniques give initially the X, Y and Z values of the internationally defined CIE system, these three coordinates being a measure of reflection in the red, green and blue regions of the visible spectrum. However, nowadays these coordinates are mathematically transformed (usually in a calculator or computer) into the CIELAB (1976) colour system using Eqns 2.2–2.4:

$$L^* = 116(Y/Y_0)^{1/3} - 16 \tag{2.2}$$

$$a^* = 500[(X/X_0)^{1/3} - (Y/Y_0)^{1/3}] \tag{2.3}$$

$$b^* = 200[(Y/Y_0)^{1/3} - (Z/Z_0)^{1/3}] \tag{2.4}$$

where X_0, Y_0 and Z_0 are the CIE tristimulus values for the reference white.

This 1976 cube-root transformation gives a more visually uniform colour space than the original (1931) XYZ space.

Coloured samples can be represented in terms of their hue and chroma on a two-dimensional colour map (or chromaticity diagram) by plotting either (xy) or (a^*b^*) coordinates defined as below:
– 1931 chromaticity coordinates: $x = X/(X+Y+Z)$; $y = Y/(X+Y+Z)$.
– 1976 chromaticity coordinates: a^*b^* (as above).

The corresponding colour maps showing the boundaries of real colours are illustrated in Figure 2.1 (1931 chromaticity diagram) and in Figure 2.2 (1976 CIELAB colour map). Note that strictly speaking any colour specification should indicate three dimensions (see discussion in Part III, section 12.1).

To quantify the magnitude of the colour difference (symbol ΔE) between two samples we must use the 1976 CIELAB coordinates (say, (L^*_1, a^*_1, b^*_1) and (L^*_2, a^*_2, b^*_2)) and calculate the answer using Eqn 2.5:

$$\Delta E = [(L^*_1 - L^*_2)^2 + (a^*_1 - a^*_2)^2 + (b^*_1 - b^*_2)^2]^{1/2}$$

$$= [(\Delta L^*)^2 + (\Delta a^*)^2 + (\Delta b^*)^2]^{1/2} \tag{2.5}$$

The relationships between ΔE and the grey scale values (1 to 5) used for assessing the change of colour in fastness testing are indicated in Table 2.1.

TABLE 2.1

Grey scale rating	ΔE (colour-difference units)
5	0
4	1.5 (slight)
3	3.0 (little)
2	6.0 (some)
1	12.0 (much)

Fastness assessments
Many of the experiments in Part II require the assessment of the fastness of the dyed material to, for example, washing, light or some other agency. These assessments should normally be carried out according to the standard methods of the International Standards Organisation (ISO) or the equivalent British Standard (BS) method, full details of the appropriate test being given in the relevant ISO or BS publication.

Note that the change of colour and degree of staining in all tests except light fastness are quoted in terms of grey scale values 5 to 1 where 5 indicates zero change or staining and 1 indicates appreciable staining or change of colour. On the other hand, light fastness is quoted on a scale of 8 to 1, representing the fastness of dyed blue wool standards of very high fastness (8) to very low light fastness (1).

In some experiments modifications or amplified versions of the standard tests are used.

2.4 SAFETY IN THE LABORATORY
In recent years attention has been increasingly, and rightly, directed towards safety in laboratories and factories and this is the subject of the Health and Safety At Work Act of 1974. More recently an approved code of practice has been drawn up for the control of substances hazardous to health (COSHH), on the basis of discussions between the Confederation of British Industry, Trades Union Congress, local authorities, government departments and the UK Health and Safety Executive. Each section in the code gives practical guidance on specific regulations. Teaching establishments will have their own safety precautions and procedures and students should familiarise themselves with these at the

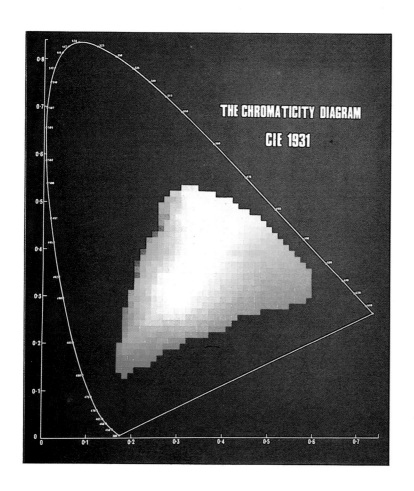

Figure 2.1 – CIE 1931 chromaticity diagram

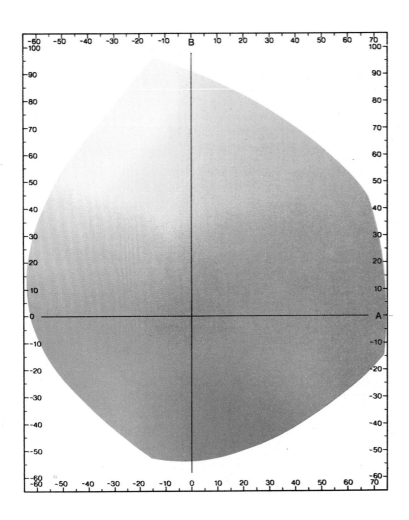

Figure 2.2 – CIE 1976 colour map (courtesy ICI plc)

beginning of their laboratory course. For detailed information on the Health and Safety Act and laboratory practice, students should refer to the bibliography at the end of this chapter. The following advice is of a general nature but also has in mind the particular experiments described later.

(a) Many laboratory chemicals, organic and inorganic, may be dangerous or toxic in some way, and in addition organic chemicals may be flammable. Sound working practice should ensure that all such materials can be used with safety.

(b) Human error is responsible for more than 80% of all laboratory accidents and these are more likely to occur with younger rather than older workers.

(c) Fire is the major hazard in a laboratory, due to the use of Bunsen burners and the likely presence of volatile and flammable organic solvents. Students should realise that closing the air valve in a Bunsen burner to produce a yellow sooty flame does *not* remove the danger. Always turn the burner off when the heating operation is complete.

(d) Personal protection is important. Safety spectacles must be worn *at all times* in the laboratory. It is good practice to keep all chemicals off the hands where possible, and wash the skin quickly if spillage does occur. Of the chemicals used in the experiments in the book, sulphuric acid (section 3.1) can cause dangerous burns on contact with skin, and even weaker organic acids, e.g. acetic acid (section 3.1), can cause burns. Sodium hydroxide (section 4.6) and ammonia also affect the skin and can cause painful burns. At all times a properly fastened laboratory coat is essential since it will provide some personal protection as well as minimising contamination of normal clothing.

(e) Always treat moving machinery with respect, even relatively simple equipment such as dyeing machines. Sometimes these may be operating under pressure (sections 5.4 and 6.3) and it is essential that no attempt should be made to open these until atmospheric pressure has been re-established.

(f) Electricity is dangerous. Check that no tubes carrying water are allowed to fall on plugs and switches, and report all electricity faults immediately.

(g) Make a practice of always checking the labels on reagent bottles for special warnings.

(h) Most organic solvents and many other organic liquids are both volatile and flammable, though few of these are used in the experiments. Dimethylformamide (DMF) used in the experiments in sections 4.5 and 8.8 is an irritant and toxic if its vapours are inhaled, while acetone (section 8.5) is flammable. Contact with phenol (section 8.6) can cause skin burns.

Since all the experiments involve the use of dyes, an attempt has been made to include only those which have no potential health hazard. In 1974 the setting up of the Ecological and Toxicological Association of the Dyestuffs Manufacturing Industry (ETAD) to monitor the safety of its products has meant that certain dyes may periodically be removed from manufacturers' ranges should these become suspect for one reason or another. In the course of time other dyes included may be removed for the same reason but, as previously pointed out, the dyes in the experiments can normally be replaced by others of the same class.

BIBLIOGRAPHY

Health and safety at work
1. J L Worsley, J.S.D.C., **94** (1978) 471.
2. 'Control of substances hazardous to health – regulations 1988' (London: HMSO, 1988).

Health and safety in the laboratory
3. T M Thompson, 'Dyehouse laboratory practice' (Bradford: SDC, 1983) 11.
4. 'Safety in laboratories', 3rd Edn (London: Ciba–Geigy, 1983).

Dyestuff toxicity
5. R Anliker, Rev. Prog. Coloration, **8** (1977) 60.
6. R Anliker and E A Clarke, J.S.D.C., **98** (1982) 42.

PART II

Experimental

3 DYES FOR WOOL

Soluble dyes for wool comprise acid, mordant and reactive dyes. These classes vary with respect to brightness, hue, fastness and ease of application, and the ultimate choice of dye to be used will depend on end use and economic factors.

3.1 ACID DYES

Acid dyes are classified broadly into the following four groups, according to their dyeing properties and wet fastness, though many dyes have intermediate properties. Thus groups (b) and (c) below may not always be clearly distinguishable.

(a) Levelling or equalising acid dyes, which require a strong acid (usually sulphuric acid is used) to give good exhaustion. They have poor fastness to washing and other wet treatments, but good levelling properties, i.e. during dyeing the dye distributes itself evenly throughout the fibres on continued treatment at the boil.

(b) Milling acid dyes, which are applied from a weakly acid bath (acetic acid is usually employed), have a good fastness to washing and wet treatments such as milling, but usually poor levelling properties.

(c) Neutral-dyeing or super-milling acid dyes which again have good fastness to washing and other more severe wet treatments, but are difficult to dye level.

(d) Metal-complex acid dyes. These are more expensive than the other tpyes of acid dyes and have a metal, usually chromium, incorporated in the dye structure during manufacture, and give dyeings with fastness properties similar to those of the super-milling and mordant dyes (section 3.9). The presence of metals such as chromium in dyes often has a beneficial effect on light fastness. There are two classes of these dyes, one in which one dye molecule is complexed with one atom of chromium (1:1 metal-complex or pre-metallised dyes) and one in which the ratio is two dye molecules to one chromium atom (1:2 metal-complex dyes). The 1:1 group of dyes is applied from a strongly acid dyebath while the 1:2 metal-complex dyes require only very weakly acidic conditions.

Acid dyes are normally applied at the boil. Glauber's salt ($Na_2SO_4 . 10H_2O$) is used to retard dyeing and thus promote levelness with dyes of type (a). However, Glauber's salt is not very effective with dyes of types (b) or (c) and indeed may even act in an opposite sense under neutral dyeing conditions; with these dyes, proprietary levelling or level-dyeing agents may be used to reduce the rate of dyeing. Anionic levelling agents act by competing with the dye for absorption by the fibre; other types, e.g. non-ionics, form a complex with the dye which releases the dye slowly for combination with the fibre.

Phosphoric acid was at one time recommended as an alternative to sulphuric acid and was said to offer several advantages in large-scale dyeing practice, causing less damage to the wool on prolonged boiling.

3.2 EFFECT OF ACIDITY ON THE UPTAKE OF ACID DYES

Acid dyes in general give high levels of exhaustion, but in the case of the levelling dyes this is often markedly dependent on pH. The following experiment illustrates this effect.

Procedure
Select a representative dye from each of the following classes (suitable examples are shown in parentheses).
(a) Levelling or equalising acid dye (C.I. Acid Red 37)
(b) Milling acid dye (C.I. Acid Blue 80)
(c) Neutral-dyeing or super-milling acid dye (C.I. Acid Blue 138).

Prepare a solution of each dye by dissolving 0.5 g of dye in boiling deionised water and dilute to 500 ml in a volumetric flask using cold deionised water. Using 5 g of scoured wool fabric prepare three dyebaths (I, II and III) for each dye containing the ingredients shown in Table 3.1.

TABLE 3.1

	Amount (% o.w.f.)		
	I	II	III
Dye	1	1	1
Glauber's salt	10	10	10
Acetic acid		1	
Sulphuric acid			3

Liquor ratio 50:1

Wet out the wool with tap water and enter into the dyebath at 40°C, raise the temperature to the boil in 20 min with constant stirring and dye at the boil for a further 30 min, stirring continuously. Rinse and dry.

The dyeing conditions vary according to the acidity of the dyebath and are based on those used in the SDC classification of acid dyes (Reports of the Committees on the Dyeing Properties of Direct Cotton, Vat and Wool Dyes).

Results
1. Note the difference in uptake of dye from the dyebaths (exhaustion of dyebaths) for each of the three dyes.
2. Suggest the most suitable dyeing method for each of (a), (b) and (c). Normally the recommended method is that which gives high exhaustion under the least acidic conditions.
3. Compare the dyeings from (a), (b) and (c) and note any differences in levelness (this is not always easy with relatively small samples).

3.3 WASH FASTNESS OF ACID DYES
Certain properties of acid dyes, such as wash fastness and migration (i.e. the ability of a dye to transfer from a more to a less heavily dyed area) can be related to the classification outlined above. Generally dyed wool is not washed at temperatures above 60°C, and many dyeings have low fastness ratings at this temperature.

Procedure

Use three portions (10 × 4 cm) of each of the dyeings of C.I. Acid Red 37, C.I. Acid Blue 80 and C.I. Acid Blue 138 obtained above. Stitch each portion between two pieces of undyed white fabric (one cotton, the other wool, each measuring 5 × 4 cm). Carry out wash fastness tests on the nine composite specimens using the conditions specified in Table 3.2. Conditions I and II represent respectively those for standard wash fastness tests ISO 2 and ISO 3, while III approximates to the conditions met with in domestic washing.

TABLE 3.2

	Concn (g/l)		
	I	II	III
Soap	5	5	
Sodium carbonate		2	
Washin powder			5
Temperature (°C)	50	60	60
Time (min)	45	30	30

Liquor ratio 50:1

Results
1. Assess the fastness to washing of the three dyes for each of the three washing conditions using the grey scales for (a) effect on pattern and (b) staining of adjacent white material.
2. Relate the results to the optimum dyeing conditions in the previous experiment.
3. Note any difference between the use of alkaline soap and a domestic washing powder, i.e. between conditions II and III.

3.4 MIGRATION PROPERTIES OF ACID DYES

Procedure

Combine a 1 g sample of each of the dyeings of C.I. Acid Red 37, C.I. Acid Blue 80 and C.I. Acid Blue 138 with a 1 g sample of undyed scoured wool and treat each pair (dyed and undyed) in a 'blank' dyebath for 30 min at the boil. The 'blank' dyebath should be identical with that found to be recommended for the respective dyes (section 3.2), without the addition of any dye.

Any dye of good migration properties should transfer from the dyed to the undyed wool under these conditions, while a dye of poor migration will leave the dyed wool almost unchanged after the experiment.

Results
1. Assess the migration properties of the three dyes using the appropriate grey scale.
2. Relate the results to the optimum dyeing conditions established previously, and to the type of dye.

3. From the *Colour Index*, find the molecular weights of the three dyes used and relate these to the various properties investigated above, i.e. acidity of the dyebath, wash fastness and migrating power.

3.5 PRODUCTION OF A RANGE OF SHADES ON WOOL

Fashion colours on ladies' dress wool garments have been traditionally produced with mixtures of levelling acid dyes. In order to produce an exact match these dyes can, if necessary, be salted on, i.e. added directly to the boiling bath, since they are readily levelled by further boiling. Most of the colours required can be obtained using mixtures of only three dyes, e.g. a bluish-red (e.g. C.I. Acid Red 1), a yellow (e.g. C.I. Acid Yellow 17) and a greenish-blue (e.g. C.I. Acid Blue 45). Orange, green and purple may be obtained when these are used in pairs. All three dyes together give a range of duller colours.

Procedure

Prepare seven dyeings on 5 g pieces of wool as shown in Table 3.3. Enter the fabric into the bath at 30°C, raise the temperature to the boil and continue dyeing for 30 min. Rinse the patterns in cold water and dry.

TABLE 3.3

	Amount (% o.w.f.)						
	I	II	III	IV	V	VI	VII
C.I. Acid Red 1	1			0.5	0.5		0.33
C.I. Acid Yellow 17		1		0.5		0.5	0.33
C.I. Acid Blue 45			1		0.5	0.5	0.33
Glauber's salt	10	10	10	10	10	10	10
Sulphuric acid	3	3	3	3	3	3	3

Liquor ratio 50:1

Results

1. Arrange the coloured patterns in the form of a colour triangle with a single colour at each corner, the binary mixtures along the corresponding sides and the ternary mixture in the middle.
2. Assess visually whether the binary colours do represent the mid-points between the three pairs of single colours, and where they do not appear as such carry out repeat dyeings with modified recipes to obtain more accurate visual representations of the mid-points. Hence establish which dye is colouristically (a) the strongest and (b) the weakest.
3. By modification of the ternary dyeing recipe, attempt to obtain a good neutral grey shade.
4. Attempt to match, with a combination of the three acid dyes, the colour of any suitable object, e.g. the colour of a book cover, wall covering, etc.

3.6 METAMERIC COLOURS

One of the difficulties encountered in carrying out colour matching using different substrates, or within the same substrate and different combinations of dyes, is that of metamerism (see section 12.5). Pairs of dyeings which match under one set of lighting conditions may appear quite different under another. This experiment illustrates the extreme of what is a very common phenomenon.

Procedure

Carry out dyeings on 5 g patterns of wool using the levelling acid dyes as shown in Table 3.4 and dye as for acid levelling dyes.

TABLE 3.4

| | Amount (% o.w.f.) | | | |
	I	II	III	IV
C.I. Acid Violet 17	0.25			0.175
C.I. Acid Yellow 3	0.05			2.5
Lissamine Fast Navy 2G150 (ICI)		0.2		
C.I. Acid Green 12		0.05	1.75	
C.I. Acid Orange 10			0.15	

Liquor ratio 50:1
Dyeings I and II and dyeings III and IV are metameric pairs

Results

Compare the two pairs of dyeings for a colour match under:
(a) Artificial daylight (D_{65}) lamp
(b) Tungsten (A) lamp
(c) Daylight, at a north-facing window if possible.

As a direct consequence of metamerism the quantities of dye shown may require slight adjustment for good colour matches to be obtained.

3.7 ACID-DYEING 1:1 METAL-COMPLEX DYES

Both the acid-dyeing 1:1 and the neutral-dyeing 1:2 metal-complex dyes combine a high degree of wet fastness with good level-dyeing properties. The 1:2 metal-complex dyes are more widely used owing to the more favourable dyebath conditions involved.

The important features of the dyeing behaviour of the 1:1 metal-complex dyes, which are used primarily on piece goods, are:
(a) High substantivity for the fibre under weakly acid conditions, but low migration powers
(b) At low pH values the equilibrium exhaustion is reduced but migration is increased considerably.

Procedure
1. Using two 5g samples of wool fabric for each dyeing, prepare three dyebaths as shown in Table 3.5. Enter two patterns into each dyebath at 50°C. Raise the temperature to the boil and dye at that temperature for 45 min.
2. Carry out a migration test using one of the 5 g samples from each dyeing and treat it, along with an equal weight of undyed scoured wool, for 45 min at the boil in a 'blank' bath with the same reagents that were used in the original dyeing.

TABLE 3.5

	Amount (% o.w.f.)		
	---	---	---
	I	II	III
C.I. Acid Red 179	2	2	2
Sulphuric acid	10	1	5
Glauber's salt			20
Non-ionic levelling agent			2

Liquor ratio 50:1

Results
1. Comment on any differences in exhaustion and levelness found between the three dyeing conditions.
2. Assess the migration properties of C.I. Acid Red 179 using the grey scale and retain each sample for a comparison with tests from other dye classes.
3. Retain a sample from the dyeing for a fastness to potting test to be carried out later (see section 3.11).

3.8 NEUTRAL-DYEING 1:2 METAL-COMPLEX DYES
These dyes are applied from a neutral or slightly acidic bath, and are characterised by high all-round fastness properties, good level-dyeing properties (which are a result of low rates of dyeing) and an ability to give non-skittery dyeings. They are used particularly for pale or medium-depth dyeings.

The earliest types of 1:2 metal-complex dyes contained no sulphonic acid groups and consequently such weakly polar dyes exhibit level-dyeing behaviour on wool of variable surface characteristics, (i.e. 'tippy' wool). Strongly polar 1:2 metal-complex acid dyes containing sulphonic acid groups are more sensitive to such variations in surface characteristics. With increasing depth the problem of fibre selectivity decreases until with, for example, dark browns and navies it ceases to be important. Hence, because unsulphonated 1:2 metal-complex dyes are expensive to manufacture, several companies have introduced small ranges of sulphonated 1:2 metal-complex dyes specifically for producing deep colours economically.

The main features of the dyeing behaviour of the unsulphonated dyes on wool are (a) high substantivity for wool under weakly acid and even neutral conditions and (b) uniform absorption under such conditions, with good coverage of tippy wool and minimum skitteriness. Level dyeing depends primarily on uniform initial uptake of dye, but some of these dyes exhibit reasonable migrating power, being superior in this respect to many neutral-dyeing non-metallised acid dyes.

The rate and extent of dye uptake are reduced by the presence of levelling agents of the cationic/non-ionic type and a number of these have been introduced for use with this class of dye, as with the milling acid dyes.

Procedure

1. Carry out the dyeings on 5 g samples as shown in Table 3.6. (C.I. Acid Yellow 114 is a metal-complex dye solubilised by a non-ionic solubilising group such as $-SO_2NH_2$ and $-SO_2CH_3$, while C.I. Acid Red 357 is a metal-complex dye containing sulphonic acid groups.) Enter the material into the bath at 50°C, work it at this temperature for 10 min, raise the temperature slowly to the boil over 45 min and continue dyeing at the boil for 30–45 min.
2. Carry out migration tests on samples from each dyeing as in section 3.7.

TABLE 3.6

	Amount (% o.w.f.)	
	I	II
C.I. Acid Yellow 114	3	
C.I. Acid Red 357		3
Ammonium acetate	5	5

Liquor ratio 50:1

Results

1. Assess the migration properties of the two dyes using the grey scale and retain these tests for later comparison with tests on other dye classes. Comment on any differences between the behaviour of the two dyes.
2. Retain a sample from each dyeing for a comparison of fastness to potting to be carried out later (see section 3.11).

3.9 MORDANT DYES (AFTERCHROME PROCESS)

Mordant dyes have particular structural features which allow them to be treated with a mordant, usually 'bichrome' (sodium or potassium dichromate), to effect considerable improvement in the wet and light fastness properties of the dyeings. This mordant may be applied before, during or after dyeing, though at present the process of applying it after dyeing, known as the afterchrome process, is the most widely used. The resulting dye–metal complex formed during this process is similar to that in the metal-complex dyes (sections 3.7 and 3.8). Mordant dyes, often referred to as chrome dyes, are used for men's wear, where their high all-round fastness properties are valuable and their comparative dullness of colour is not a disadvantage. However effluent problems have to be considered.

Variations in colour and fastness sometimes occur when the afterchrome method is used. These are due to differences in the relative proportions of 1:1 and 1:2 chromium–dye complexes formed in the fibre. The proportions tend to vary according to the nature of the acid used, a higher proportion of the 1:2 complex being formed when acetic acid is used alone rather than when used in conjunction with formic acid.

Some types of dyes applied by the afterchrome process are sparingly soluble in water at room temperatures and are marketed as dispersible powders. The main advantage claimed for these dyes is that, since they are almost completely out of solution at the beginning of dyeing and therefore are not substantive, markedly improved control of dye adsorption is possible and level, well penetrated dyeings can be produced more easily.

The metachrome process, also known as the chromate or monochrome process, is the simplest method of applying mordant dyes, but can be employed only with a limited number of dyes. A mixture of potassium dichromate and ammonium sulphate, made just alkaline with ammonia, is used as the mordant, which is included in the dyebath itself. Dyeing and mordanting take place simultaneously.

The chrome mordant process is the oldest of the processes for applying mordant dyes but it is no longer used. It was a lengthier process and therefore less economical. Potassium or sodium dichromate was applied (a) without other addition (sweet chrome mordant), (b) in the presence of sulphuric acid (sour chrome mordant), which gave better exhaustion of the mordant, or (c) in the presence of an organic acid, e.g. formic acid or tartaric acid (reduced chrome mordant), which, though more expensive, gave brighter colours with some dyes.

The following experiment illustrates the application of mordant dyes by the after-chrome process.

Procedure
Dye a 10 g piece of wool in each of the dyebaths made up as shown in Table 3.7. Enter the wetted wool into the dyebath at about 40°C, raise the temperature to the boil and continue dyeing for a further 30 min. Then add 2% formic acid (85%) and continue boiling until exhaustion is almost complete.

TABLE 3.7

	Amount (% o.w.f.)	
	I	II
C.I. Mordant Orange 6	2	
C.I. Mordant Black 7		2
Glauber's salt	10	10
Acetic acid	3	3

Liquor ratio 50:1

Aftertreatment (chroming)

1. Remove the dyed wool from the dyebath and cut off a sample (approx. 3 g) as a record of the dyeings at this stage. Carry out the afterchroming by adding 1% potassium dichromate and 50 ml cold water to the existing dyebath. Replace the previously dyed patterns in the dyebath at 70°C, raise the temperature to the boil and treat at this temperature for a further 30 min.
2. For each dye, using portions from both the 'untreated' and 'aftertreated' dyeings, carry out wash fastness (ISO 3) and light fastness tests according to the standard procedures.
3. Carry out a migration test on one of the dyes as in section 3.7.

Results

1. For each dye, compare the dyeings before and after the 'chroming' treatment, along with the samples removed during aftertreatment. Students with a knowledge of dye chemistry should attempt to find out the structures of the two dyes and to explain the observed differences in behaviour of the two dyes during 'chroming'.
2. For each dye, assess the wash fastness (grey scales) and light fastness (blue wool standards) of the 'untreated' and 'aftertreated' dyeing. Comment on the changes observed.
3. Retain a sample of the aftertreated dyeing for a fastness to potting test to be carried out later (see section 3.11).
4. Assess the migrational properties of the dye using the appropriate grey scale and retain these samples for comparison in tests on other dye classes.

3.10 REACTIVE DYES

Certain difficulties were encountered that limited the early use of reactive dyes on wool. It was not possible to achieve complete reaction of dye and fibre, and any dye not chemically combined would be slowly removed from the fibre and so reduce the fastness of the dyeings to wet treatments. Furthermore, reactive dyes are very sensitive to variations in the nature of the fibre surface. This particular characteristic would not matter if the dyes exhibited high migrating power, but since no further movement of dye is possible once dye–fibre reaction has taken place and reaction commences as soon as the dye has been adsorbed on the fibre, initially skittery dyeings do not level as dyeing is prolonged. Some improvements in dyeing behaviour are achieved by applying reactive dyes in the presence of specific levelling auxiliaries.

The Lanasol (CGY) dyes provide a range of bright dyeings of very good fastness to light and wet treatments. An essential ingredient of the dyebath is Albegal B (CGY); this promotes level dyeing, but unlike other products it is amphoteric and highly substantive to the fibre and increases the rate of dyeing. Addition of sodium sulphate to the dyebath is essential to ensure the maximum effectiveness of the Albegal B. The Lanasol dyes combine with the fibre by a nucleophilic addition reaction, but do not hydrolyse in the dyebath under the recommended conditions of dyeing. Hence only a small proportion of the dye on the fibre at the end of the dyeing remains uncombined. Nevertheless, with dyeings deeper than medium depth, or where very high fastness to wet treatments is required, as much as possible of this uncombined dye should be removed by raising the pH towards the end of the dyeing by adding ammonia and treating the material at pH 8–8.5 for 10–15 min at 70–80°C.

The introduction of machine-washable wool goods has meant that dyeings now must be able to withstand washing treatments more severe than those traditionally carried out.

Reactive dyes have become pre-eminent in providing the fastness properties required for the 'machine-washable' label, as well as giving a desirable range of bright colours.

Procedure
Produce a dyeing on 5 g of wool as follows:
– C.I. Reactive Red 65, 2%
– Acetic acid, 3%
– Ammonium sulphate, 2%
– Albegal B, 1.5%
Liquor ratio 50:1.

Add the acetic acid and ammonium sulphate to the bulk of the water. Dilute the Albegal B (levelling agent) separately with water and add it to the dyebath (Check that the pH is in the range 4–5). Heat to 50°C and treat the material in the blank dyebath at this temperature for 10 min. Lift out the pattern, add the dissolved dye and re-enter the pattern. Raise the temperature to the boil over 20 min and dye for a further 45 min. Add ammonia (0.5–1.0% of sp. gr. 0.880) to the existing dyebath to give a pH of about 8.5 and treat the material in a cooling bath for 15 min. Wash thoroughly.

Results
1. Carry out a migration test on the dyed pattern as described in section 3.7.
2. Retain a sample of the dyeing for a fastness to potting test to be carried out as below (section 3.11).
3. The reactive grouping in the Lanasol dyes is $-NHCOC(Br)=CH_2$. Students of organic chemistry should attempt to show the nature of the chemical reaction between the dye and the wool, and explain how the presence of the bromine substituent in the dye assists in this reaction.

3.11 FASTNESS TO POTTING
Potting is a high-temperature aqueous treatment carried out on certain high-quality woollen cloths to improve their finish and handle. The ISO colour fastness to potting test is intended to determine the resistance of dyed wool to the action of boiling water and is a very severe one. The following experiment is based on this test and compares the resistance to severe wet treatments of most of the types of dye commonly applied to wool.

Procedure
Prepare a small piece of each of the dyeings mentioned in sections 3.7–3.10 along with one described in section 3.5 for testing the fastness to potting as follows.

Cut a sample 10 × 4 cm from each dyeing. Place each dyed sample between a sample of undyed wool and one of white cotton of the same size and sew all three together along one of the shorter sides. Roll this composite sample round a glass rod to form a cylinder 4 cm long and tie it loosely with thread.

Treat the composite specimen in boiling water (distilled) for 60 min under reflux. Separate the treated specimen into its components and dry these.

Results
Assess the relative fastness to potting of the five dye classes, using the grey scales.

3.12 SUPERWASH WOOL

Superwash wool is treated in such a manner as to impart the property of machine washability upon it. The main prerequisite for this is shrink resistance coupled with adequate fastness properties. Many silicone elastomers and resins are used for this treatment, and the following experiment illustrates the effect of a typical resin, Hercosett 57 (Hercules), on the dyeing and fastness properties of wool dyed with three different classes of dyes.

Treatment first involves mild acid chlorination, followed by application of a cationic epichlorohydrin resin from aqueous solution onto the surface scales of the wool.

As well as imparting shrink resistance, the Hercosett 57 treatment affects the dyeing characteristics of wool. Hercosett 57-treated wool has a much greater substantivity for anionic dyes than has untreated wool, the main reason for this being the high basicity of the resin caused by the presence of the azetidinium cation (Figure 3.1) and because the wool surface is made more hydrophilic by the chlorination process.

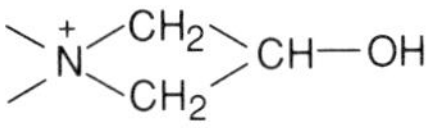

Figure 3.1

Procedure

1. Take four 5 g pieces of Hercosett-treated wool and for 2 g pieces of untreated wool and pretreat separately, at a liquor ratio of 50:1, in a solution of 1% non-ionic detergent and 1% sodium carbonate for 15 min at 50°C. Rinse well with water. This treatment neutralises any acidity caused by the Hercosett 57 treatment.

TABLE 3.8

| | Amount (% o.w.f.) | | | |
	I V	II VI	III VII	IV VIII
C.I. Reactive Red 65	2			
C.I. Reactive Red 2		2		
C.I. Acid Red 1 (acid levelling)			2	
C.I. Acid Red 259 (metal-complex)				2
Glauber's salt			15	
Ammonium sulphate	4			3
Albegal B	1			
Acetic acid	(to pH 5)	(to pH 3)		
Sulphuric acid			3	

Liquor ratio 50:1
I–IV untreated and V–VIII treated

2. Carry out dyeings as shown in Table 3.8. Start dyeing at 50°C and raise to the boil (over approx. 30 min). Boil for 45 min. Remove small portions from each dyeing after 1, 5, 10, 20 and 60 min from the commencement of dyeing. With the exception of dyeings I and V rinse with cold water and dry. With dyeings I and V cool the dyebath to 80°C and increase the pH to 8–8.5 with dilute ammonia solution. Rinse and dry as before. Raising the pH removes any unreacted dye from the fibres.
3. By cutting pieces from each of the eight dyed samples, carry out ISO 3 fastness to washing tests on each, i.e. 30 min at 60°C for in 5 g/l soap and 2 g/l sodium carbonate at a liquor ratio of 50:1. Assess the fastness to light of the dyed samples I and V against the blue wool standards 1 to 8.

Results
1. Compare and assess the effect of Hercosett 57 treatment on the following:
   (a) Rate of dye uptake during dyeing with each type of dye
   (b) Fastness to washing (ISO 3) by means of the grey scales
   (c) Fastness to light using samples from dyeings I and V.
2. Comment on the suitability of each class of dye for the 'Superwash' label.

3.13   EFFECT OF THE SURFACE CHARACTERISTICS OF WOOL ON ITS DYEING BEHAVIOUR

Modification of the surface of wool fibres such as occurs at the tips during exposure on the sheep's back or on the surface of cloth when it is abraded, and more generally when wool is chlorinated, considerably affects the dyeing behaviour of the material. This modification involves the partial removal of the hydrophobic epicuticle, the extremely thin outermost covering of the scales on the fibre surface, which normally acts as a barrier to the entry of dye into the fibre. In extreme cases the scales themselves (the cuticle) may be partially removed; this facilitates local penetration of the fibres by dyes, particularly highly anionic dyes, and tippy or skittery dyeings are obtained.

The effect on dyeing behaviour of modifying the surface characteristics of wool can be readily demonstrated using polysulphonated acid dyes, which under normal dyeing

TABLE 3.9

| | Amount (% o.w.f.) | | | |
	I	II	III	IV
C.I. Acid Blue 47	0.5	0.5		
C.I. Acid Red 18			0.25	0.25
Matexil LC-CWL		3		3
Glauber's salt	10	10	10	10
Acetic acid (30%)	1	1	1	1

Liquor ratio 50:1

conditions are much more rapidly adsorbed by the modified fibres. Addition to the dyebath of certain weakly cationic auxiliary products, e.g. Matexil LC-CWL (ICI), significantly reduces the selective dyeing behaviour of such anionic dyes and, by using 1–3% of Matexil LC-CWL, the time required to obtain satisfactory solidity of shade is considerably reduced. This effect is demonstrated in the experiment described below.

Abrasion of cloth already dyed produces light patches. This is due to the increased reflection of light from the abraded areas.

Procedure

Take four 5 g pieces of wool fabric and abrade half of each pattern by rubbing with glass paper. Carry out dyeing as shown in Table 3.9. Start the dyeings at 40°C. Raise the temperature to the boil in 30 min and continue dyeing at the boil for 40 min. Observe the samples at regular intervals, noting the degree of the contrast between the abraded and unabraded areas.

Results

1. Compare dyeings I and III and if possible identify the polysulphonated dye. One dye is monosulphonated and the other trisulphonated.
2. Comment on the effect of the auxiliary on both dyes by examination of the pairs of dyeings I and II, and III and IV.

4 DYES FOR CELLULOSIC FIBRES

Despite the tremendous growth of synthetic-polymer fibres, cotton still accounts for nearly half of the total world fibre production, though a large amount of cotton is now used in fabric blends with polyester.

The major classes of dye used in the dyeing of cellulosic fibres are sulphur, direct, vat, reactive and azoic dyes. The most important, in terms of quantity used in cotton dyeing (although not in terms of the quantity of cotton dyed), are the sulphur dyes, where cost-effectiveness is coupled with good fastness properties. Sulphur dyes are, however, more difficult to apply than the next most important class, direct dyes, and are also more restricted in their range of hues than are the latter. The relatively poor wash-fastness of direct dyes limits their usage to those areas where this factor is of secondary importance, e.g. in curtain linings, where fast-to-light directs are ideal, combining cost-effectiveness with excellent light fastness. If the highest wet fastness is required then vat, reactive and azoic dyes may be used where the colouristic properties of the sulphur class are inadequate.

Vat dyes have excellent all-round fastness properties but are expensive and must be applied, like many sulphur dyes, in the reduced or leuco form and subsequently oxidised *in situ*. Reactive dyes are important both in printing and in dyeing, providing a wide range of colours of good all round fastness, while azoic dyes still retain an important place in dyeing and printing despite the limitations of shade and method of application.

Clearly the final choice of dye class in cotton dyeing will be determined by economics and in-service requirements, and the following experiments illustrate the application of these main dye classes to cotton as well as some less widely used (e.g. Phthalogen and Indosol dyes). For a comprehensive treatment of the dyeing of cellulosic fibres reference should be made to the recent SDC textbook on the subject [1].

4.1 EFFECTS OF SALT CONCENTRATION AND LIQUOR RATIO ON THE UPTAKE OF DIRECT DYES

Direct dyes are widely employed commercially in the cheaper types of cotton and viscose goods for the dyeing of garments, furnishings, linings and carpets. A very wide range is available, but the fastness properties are often not of the highest order, unless some aftertreatment of the dyeing (cf. section 4.2) is performed. These aftertreatments are normally carried out to improve fastness to washing and some may have an adverse effect on light fastness. Special ranges of direct dyes of excellent fastness to light are also available. These have superior properties to the more usual dye types, though they are more expensive, and are used typically for furnishings, garments and sewing cotton for men's suitings.

Direct dyes remain one of the simplest classes of dyes to use. They are water soluble and can be applied to natural cellulosic and viscose fibres by simply heating the material in a dye solution, preferably with the addition of common salt or Glauber's salt. The rate at which the dye is adsorbed on the fibre and the amount that has been absorbed when the dyeing operation is complete are determined not only by the intrinsic substantivity of the dye for the fibre but also by the amount of salt used, the liquor ratio of the dyebath, and its temperature. Adding salt to the bath improves its exhaustion. So also does an increase in the concentration of dye in the bath; this means that exhaustion, or uptake of dye by the fibre, can be improved without the use of additional dye, simply by using less water in the bath, i.e. by reducing the liquor ratio. This may not always be possible, however, since the use of low liquor ratios may cause operational difficulties. An increase in dyeing temperature increases the rate at which the dye is taken up and also the rate at which it migrates or levels when on the fibre; but it is important to note that a rise in temperature also reduces the equilibrium exhaustion (see Figure 10.2).

Procedure
Prepare three dyebaths as shown in Table 4.1. Make up the baths by adding dye solution, and salt if required, to each bath at 40°C, then add a 10 g skein of cotton yarn or piece of cotton fabric. Raise the temperature to about 95°C and thereafter maintain the bath at this temperature for 30 min, taking care to maintain the volume of the bath by additions of water at about 95°C. Remove the patterns, rinse well in cold water and dry. Retain dyeing I for use in the next experiment.

TABLE 4.1

	Amount (% o.w.f.)		
	I[(a)]	II[(a)]	III[(b)]
C.I. Direct Green 27	2	2	2
Common salt	20		

Liquor ratio: (a) 50:1
              (b) 10:1

Results
1. By examining the depth of the dyeings, assess the effects of salt concentration and liquor ratio on the exhaustion of C.I. Direct Green 27.
2. Check these assessments by carrying out further dyeings to match dyeing I using the dyebath conditions for II and III with increased amounts of dye.

4.2 EFFECT OF AFTERTREATMENT ON THE WASH FASTNESS OF A DIRECT DYE
As a class, direct dyes have low fastness to wet treatments, e.g. washing and water, and some are not fast to light. Several aftertreatments are used to improve these properties, each process being suitable for selected dyes. The following have been used with direct dyes for the purposes indicated.

To improve fastness to washing
(a) Formaldehyde
(b) Nitrous acid (i.e. a diazotisation process) followed by treatment with a coupling component
(c) A diazotised base for direct coupling

To improve fastness to water and (with some reagents) to washing also
(d) A proprietary cationic fixing agent

To improve fastness to light and washing
(e) Copper sulphate or a proprietary copper-containing compound (or potassium dichromate may be used with a few dyes).

Some aftertreatments may change the hue of the dyeing considerably. This experiment illustrates the effect of a proprietory cationic fixing agent on the wash and light fastness of a direct dye.

Procedure
1. From dyeing I in section 4.1 retain a small sample (approx. 1 g) for comparison test purposes (control). Split the remainder into 2×4.5 g patterns and treat one in a bath containing 2% Matexil FC-PN (ICI) for 30 min at 40°C. Rinse and dry.
2. Test the wash fastness of both the untreated and the aftertreated pattern by sewing a 2 g portion between pieces of undyed wool and undyed cotton (10×4 cm) and treating the resultant sandwich samples in 150 ml soap solution (2 g/l) for 30 min at 40°C. (This is the basis of the ISO 1 wash fastness test.)
3. Carry out a light fastness test on small portions of the treated and untreated dyeings along with the blue wool standards

Results
1. Assess the relative fastness of the aftertreated and untreated dyeings using the grey scales for effect on pattern (relative to the control sample) and for staining of adjacent cotton and wool.
2. Compare the fastness to light of the treated dyeing with that of the aftertreated dyeing, using the blue wool standards.

4.3 LEVEL-DYEING PROPERTIES OF DIRECT DYES
The Society of Dyers and Colourists has devised a number of tests for the classification of direct dyes according to their dyeing properties on cellulosic fibres. The dyes are thus divided into three classes according to their levelling properties and salt controllability.[1]

Class A – Dyes having good levelling or migration properties. In general, the direct dyes with the best levelling properties are those which show maximum exhaustion at relatively low temperatures (60–80°C).

Class B – Dyes of poor levelling or migration properties, but of high salt controllability

---

1. Salt controllability is used to indicate the degree to which the adsorption or exhaustion of a dye can be controlled by means of salt added to the dyebath. A dye with low salt controllability is significantly affected by low salt concentrations, i.e. the dye is highly salt sensitive. A dye with a low degree of salt sensitivity is therefore one of high salt controllability. In the following experiment Part 1 differentiates a class A dye from classes B and C. Part 2 shows the difference between B and C class dyes.

Class C – Dyes of poor levelling and migration properties with low salt controllability.

Part 1

Procedure
Using three 5 g pieces of cotton fabric, each cut exactly in half, carry out dyeings as shown in Table 4.2. Enter the wetted fabric to the cold dyebath, raise the temperature to the boil in about 15 min. Maintain this temperature, with agitation, for 30 min. Allow to cool. Remove one of the 2.5 g halves from each dyebath and replace it with an undyed wetted 2.5 g portion of the same fabric. Raise the temperature as before, boil gently for 30 min. Rinse then dry.

TABLE 4.2

	Amount (% o.w.f.)		
	I	II	III
C.I. Direct Red 75	1		
C.I. Direct Red 79		1	
C.I. Direct Red 148			1
Common salt	20	20	20

Liquor ratio 30:1

Results
Identify which of the three red direct dyes is a class A dye.

Part 2

Procedure
Dye two 2.5 g pieces of cotton fabric with the B or C class dyes, using 1% dye and 1% common salt at a liquor ratio of 30:1. Enter the pieces dry to the gently boiling dyebath. Dye for 30 min. Remove, then squeeze excess liquor back into the respective dyebaths, rinse and dry. To the partially exhausted dyebaths add a further 20% salt, and a fresh 2.5 g piece of cotton. Dye for 30 min. Rinse and dry.

Results
Compare each pair of dyeings and classify the dyes accordingly as B or C.

Note
Class B direct dyes have high salt controllability and low sensitivity. This dye type will therefore require a high salt concentration before dyebath exhaustion is significantly affected. With dyes of this class the first piece of material entered will take up the least amount of dye.

Class C dyes have low salt controllability and high sensitivity. This means that even a very small amount of salt present will significantly increase dyebath exhaustion. The first piece of material entered to this dyebath will therefore be most heavily dyed.

In some cases the distinction between classes B and C may not be apparent using the above procedure. Students should consult the methods of testing the dyeing properties of various classes of dyes recommended in the reports of the relevant SDC committees.

4.4 COMPATIBILITY OF DIRECT DYES IN MIXTURES

Compatibility, i.e. equality in dyeing rates, of dyes in mixtures is necessary in dyeing long runs of material in a small volume of liquor; this is frequently carried out on the type of machine known as a jig or jigger. If the dyes used are not compatible they will produce ending or tailing, i.e. a difference in hue between the two ends of the material. This experiment demonstrates the difference in dyeing properties between mixtures of compatible and of non-compatible direct dyes.

Procedure

Prepare four dyebaths as shown in Table 4.3. Heat each dyebath to 85–90°C. Take six 5 g samples of bleached white cotton for each dyebath and insert one pattern in each bath, stir well for 2 min and then remove, rinse and dry. Repeat for each of the remaining five patterns in each dyebath for 2, 4, 8, 16 and 30 min respectively, removing each pattern before entering the next.

TABLE 4.3

	Amount (% o.w.f.)			
	I	II	III	IV
C.I. Direct Yellow 44	1		1	
C.I. Direct Yellow 46		1		1
C.I. Direct Blue 78	1	1		
C.I. Diect Blue106			1	1
Common salt	10	10	10	10

Liquor ratio 30:1

Results

1. Select from the four sets of dyeings the most compatible combination on the basis of uniformity of hue throughout the six patterns.
2. From the *Colour Index*, or manufacturers' pattern books, find the SDC classification (A, B or C) for the four direct dyes used, and relate these if possible to the findings in 1.

4.5 THE INDOSOL (S) DYEING SYSTEM

The Indosol dyes comprise a new range of reactant-fixable direct dyes for cellulose, which are subsequently fixed to the fibre using a special cationic agent. This agent differs from the normal cationic fixing agents used in that it involves a form of dye–fibre reaction and in addition, cross-linking of the cellulose takes place, giving excellent crease resistance and dimensional stability. The important features of the dyeing system are the simple application technique, the relatively low cost of the dyes used and the high standard of wet fastness achieved.

The following experiment illustrates the use of these dyes and compares their very high fastness to washing with that of an ordinary direct dye.

Procedure

1. Use 5 g pieces of white cotton fabric and prepare dyebaths as in Table 4.4. Start the dyeings at 40°C, raise the temperature to the boil (approx. 20 min), add salt at the boil and continue dyeing for a further 30 min. Rinse in cold water. The fixation stage is carried out in practice by a padding (continuous) process followed by curing, but the effect produced by fixation can be illustrated more simply in the laboratory.

TABLE 4.4

	Amount (% o.w.f.)		
	I	II	III
Indosol Yellow SFGL (160%)	2		
Indosol Navy SFBL (240%)		2	
C.I. Direct Blue 78			2
Common salt (g/l)	10	10	10

Liquor ratio 30:1

2. Split each pattern into three parts and keep one part as reference. Treat one of the remaining two portions of each dyeing as follows. Make up a solution (approx. 100 ml) of 130 g/l Indosol CR (S) liquid and insert the three patterns for 10 s. Remove, squeeze and dry at normal temperatures (below 100°C) and then cure for 1 min in an oven set at 170°C.
3. Test the fastness to washing at 95°C of the three pairs (two Indosol dyes, one conventional direct dye, fixed and unfixed) by preparing composite specimens in which the dyeing is sandwiched between undyed pieces of cotton and viscose fabric. Treat the composite specimens for 30 min at 95°C in a solution of 5 g/l soap and 2 g/l sodium carbonate at a liquor ratio of 50:1.
4. The fact that some form of dye–fibre reaction has taken place can be shown by boiling a sample of unfixed and fixed dyeings of both the Indosol and the direct dyes for 2 h in a reflux or thimble condenser system with a solution of 1:1 dimethylformamide/water (avoid inhalation or contact with skin).

Results

1. Assess the fastness to washing at 95°C of the Indosol dyes and compare the results with those of the direct dye chosen.

2. Compare the relative improvements in wash fastness brought about by fixation for both the Indosol and the direct dyes.
3. Compare the effect of the dimethylformamide/water treatment on stripping the dye from the pairs of fixed and unfixed dyeings. Comment on the differences observed between Indosol dyes and the direct dye.
4. Comparisons should be made with the results of the experiment described in section 4.2.

4.6 VAT DYES AND THEIR DYEING PROPERTIES

These dyes are derived from anthraquinone or from indigo (or thioindigo) and are distinguished by their excellent all-round fastness properties on cotton. Vat dyes are used for dyeings and prints of the very highest fastness to light and washing on all cellulosic fibres, e.g. for handkerchiefs, shirting, embroidery yarns, effect threads and furnishing fabrics. Indigo itself has become important again in recent times for the dyeing of denim jeans. The dyes are insoluble in water and non-substantive, but by reduction with sodium dithionite (hydrosulphite) in the presence of sodium hydroxide they are converted into substantive alkali-soluble leuco compounds, in which form they are applied to cellulose. After dyeing, the material must be oxidised to regenerate the parent insoluble dye, either by exposure to air or by the use of an oxidising agent.

A number of vat dyes are also marketed as 'solubilised' vat dyes. These are not only soluble in water, but, unlike the solubilised sulphur dyes, are substantive to cellulose and other fibres. Solubilised vat dyes are sodium salts of the sulphuric acid esters of leuco vat dyes and when they have been applied to the fibre, they are converted into the parent insoluble vat dye inside the fibre by hydrolysis and oxidation. The dyeing thus produced is indistinguishable from that obtained by using the parent dye in the normal way. Solubilised vats, despite being costly, still find considerable use in the continuous dyeing of pale shades, where they combine low substantivity (ideal for continuous processes) with optimum wet and light fastness. In addition the awkward reducing stage, necessary in continuous dyeing with vat dyes, is avoided.

Certain vat dyes exhibit tendering activity. This fault, which occurs principally with certain yellow, orange and red vat dyes, takes the form of chemical attack on the cellulose fibre, causing severe weakening (tendering) when the dyed fibre is exposed to light. A related phenomenon is the catalytic fading of vat dyes which are normally of good light fastness, caused by the presence of an 'active' dye. The remedy, for materials likely to be exposed to light in use, lies in the careful selection of dyes to avoid 'active' types.

Because of the outstanding properties of vat dyes and their suitability for continuous application techniques, a number of methods is available for their application, though all of these involve, at some stage, the reduction of the vat dye to its substantive leuco form. Recently, however, methods have been developed for the application of vat dyes in pigment form to cotton and polyester/cotton blends by continuous and batchwise methods.

The final stages of dyeing always involve oxidation followed by a treatment in boiling soap or detergent solution. Soaping is essential to obtain satisfactory dyeings and this process removes loose particles of oxidised dye from the fibre surface, thus improving the fastness to rubbing, and by causing changes in the crystal structure of the dye particles inside the fibre improves the fastness of the dyeing to various agencies such as bleaching and light.

For purposes of conventional leuco dyeing the anthraquinone vat dyes may be divided into four classes, on the basis of the amounts of sodium hydroxide required and the most suitable temperature for dyeing, but more simply they may be divided into warm- and cold-dyeing types. The warm-dyeing dyes colour cellulose readily and are applied at 50–60°C, without additions of salt. The cold-dyeing types dye less rapidly; they are applied at 25–30°C, with addition of salt. If a cold-dyeing dye is applied at a warm temperature it will produce a weaker shade than by the correct procedure. The SDC report on the dyeing properties of vat dyes should be consulted for descriptions of tests for ascertaining the most appropriate dyeing method for a given vat dye, and its rate of migration and strike. The following experiment is based on the above report and illustrates the importance of temperature on the application of vat dyes of different dyeing types.

Procedure
Since vat dyes are insoluble in water, stock preparations are thus in the form of aqueous dispersions. Consequently when taking portions from these stock dispersions, it is essential that the latter be well shaken to avoid the settling of heavier dye particles. The use of a little ethanol to paste the dye may help in the preparation of the stock dispersion.

Using 5 or 10 g skeins of cotton yarn, prepare nine dyebaths using:
– C.I. Vat Green 1, 1.2%
– C.I. Vat Orange 3, 5.0%
– C.I. Vat Brown 3, 4.2%.

Apply each of these dyes under the conditions given in Table 4.5. Enter the wetted out skeins into the dyebaths at the required temperatures and continue dyeing at these temperatures for 30 min. To prevent premature oxidation by air, try to ensure that the skeins are kept submerged in the dyebaths during dyeing. The dyebaths must be in a fully reduced state during the dyeing cycle and this can be checked for by testing with Caledon

TABLE 4.5

	Concn (g/l)		
	I[a]	II[b]	III[c]
[1]Sodium hydroxide	8	6	3.5
[1]Sodium dithionite (hydrosulphite)	4	4	4
Common salt		10	20

Liquor ratio 25:1
Temperature (°C): (a) 70
　　　　　　　　(b) 55
　　　　　　　　(c) 25

1. In practice vat dyes are first 'vatted' (reduced) to convert them to the soluble leuco compound, the suitable form for dyeing. This is best done by adding to the required volume of each dye suspension, on a water-bath at about 60°C, about two-thirds of the quantity of sodium hydroxide and sodium dithionite indicated in the table, and maintaining at this temperature until 'vatting' (reduction) is complete. This is indicated by the appearance of a true solution, often of a different colour from the original vat dye. On a small scale, such as employed here, a few minutes should suffice to ensure complete reduction. The remaining sodium hydroxide and sodium dithionite, along with water required to bring the total volume (including 'vatting' bath) to a liquor ratio of 25:1, now constitutes the dyebath.

Yellow or 'hydros' paper. When tested with a drop of the dyebath, the paper should immediately turn a deep blue, indicating that satisfactory dyebath conditions exist.

At the end of the dyeing, remove the skeins, wash thoroughly in running cold water to remove excess sodium hydroxide, squeeze and hang in the air to oxidise. Note the effect of oxidation on the colour of the dyeing, particularly with C.I. Vat Green 1 and C.I. Vat Orange 3 due to regeneration of the original insoluble vat dye *in situ*. Finally treat each dyeing in boiling soap solution (2 g/l soap) for 15 min, rinse and dry. This final soaping assists in the removal of loose dye and the development of the true colour.

Results
1. Examine the dyeings for each dye carried out at the three different temperatures. Note which dye is most affected by temperature and which could be applied over a range of temperatures. It is preferable not to mix dyes of differing dyeing types though it is not always possible to avoid this in practice.
2. By untwisting the yarns, note any differences in 'penetration', i.e. the ability of a dye to diffuse completely through yarns. The rate of diffusion of dyes, like that of any other chemical reaction, is increased with increasing temperature.
3. If desired, the fastness to washing at 95°C (ISO 4) of the vat dyes can be compared with that of a direct dye under the same conditions. Vat dyes have the highest all-round fastness of any dye class on cellulosic fibres.

4.7 SULPHUR DYES
Sulphur dyes are widely used on cotton goods for fast colours, mostly blacks, browns and deep blues, e.g. for overalls, as well as in blends of cellulosic fibres with polyester and, less importantly, with polyamide and acrylic. Although the dyes cover a fair range of hues, there is no true red, and the other colours are in general duller than the corresponding ones obtainable with vat, reactive and azoic dyes.

Sulphur dyes are applied to the fibre as substantive leuco compounds in the same manner as vat dyes (see section 4.6), and are converted into insoluble polydisulphides inside the fibre by exposing the dyeings to air or by treating them with a chemical oxidising agent. The light fastness of dyeings varies throughout the range and while wet fastness is generally good, fastness to chlorine is, with a few exceptions, poor.

The dyes are manufactured by heating sulphur with aromatic amines, phenols or aminophenols, although little is known of their actual structure. They are marketed in three distinct forms, described in the *Colour Index* as follows.

C.I. Sulphur dyes
These are insoluble or sparingly soluble in water and, as such, are non-substantive or only slightly substantive towards cellulosic fibres. They are converted into soluble, substantive leuco compounds by treatment with a reducing agent (vatting) and are then applied to the material.

C.I. Leuco Sulphur dyes
These are sulphur dyes that have been converted into the leuco form by the dye maker and are marketed as such, often in liquid form. The dyebath is prepared by diluting them with water and, as necessary, a little reducing agent.

C.I. Solubilised Sulphur dyes
These are highly water-soluble thiosulphonic acid derivatives of sulphur dyes. They are

non-substantive to the fibre but are converted into the substantive thiol form by a reducing agent. After dyeing they are converted into the original insoluble sulphur dye in the fibre by oxidation.

The most convenient reducing agent for converting sulphur dyes to the alkali-soluble leuco form is sodium sulphide, which also gives an alkaline solution in which the leuco compounds dissolve readily. The fused form of sodium sulphide is normally used, and where the presence in the dyebath of any insoluble matter is undesirable the purest possible form of sodium sulphide is preferred. One drawback to the use of sodium sulphide is that it is strongly alkaline and dyeing under such conditions can impair the physical properties of the material, particularly viscose fibre. The use of sodium hydrosulphide (NaHS) has been advocated as an alternative since the resulting dyebaths are less alkaline. One advantage of the liquid forms of leuco sulphur dyes, referred to above, is that they are buffered to give less alkaline dyebaths. A mixture of sodium dithionite and sodium carbonate may also be used as an alternative to sodium sulphide, but this is much more expensive, and normally is only used for the solubilised types.

Because of the low substantivity of the leuco forms of sulphur dyes for cellulosic fibres, additions of large amounts of common salt are made to increase dye uptake, and standing baths are often used for black shades.

Air oxidation is usually sufficient to regenerate the original insoluble dye, but chemical oxidation is used with certain dyes if the brightest results are required. A variety of oxidation treatments is given to dyeings of sulphur dyes, of which traditionally the most important are those using copper sulphate or potassium dichromate in acetic acid solution, which markedly increase the fastness of certain dyes to wet and light treatments. Because of effluent problems, other oxidising agents are now used, including hydrogen peroxide and sodium perborate. All of these reagents give slightly different effects and as a general rule per-compounds give dyeings of slightly inferior wet fastness. Certain resin finishes are also applied to improve wet fastness properties.

Black sulphur dyes in particular tended at one time to cause weakening of cellulosic fibres in dyed materials stored for prolonged periods in a hot damp atmosphere, but such tendering activity is now far less frequently encountered. This is possibly due to the use of purer dyes and sodium sulphide, and the use of stainless steel machinery.

The following experiment illustrates the differences in the dyeing procedures between sulphur and leuco sulphur dyes.

TABLE 4.6

	Amount (% o.w.f.)		
	I	II	III
C.I. Sulphur Black 1	30		
C.I. Leuco Sulphur Brown 10		5	5
Common salt	30	10	10

Liquor ratio 50:1

Procedure
1. Using 5 g pieces of white cotton, prepare three dyebaths as shown in Table 4.6.
2. To dissolve C.I. Sulphur Black 1, paste 1 g of the dye with 15 ml sodium sulphide solution (10% anhydrous or 20% crystals) and 5 ml sodium carbonate solution (10%). Boil for 1 min and add hot water (60°C) to bring the volume to 100 ml. Cool before measuring out for the dyebath. To dissolve C.I. Leuco Sulphur Brown 10, add the required amount of dye to cold water. Boiling is not necessary.
3. Add the wetted out pieces of cotton into the cold dyebaths. Raise the temperature to 90°C, adding the salt gradually during this period, and dye at this temperature for 30 min. Rinse the patterns and allow to oxidise in the air for 5 min.
4. Treat one of the two dyeings of C.I. Leuco Sulphur Brown 10, at a liquor ratio of 50:1, with sodium dichromate (4 g/l) and glacial acetic acid (3 g/l) for 10 min at 60°C. Rinse.
5. Carry out light and wash (ISO 4) fastness tests on the three completed dyeings (C.I. Sulphur Black 1 and C.I. Sulphur Brown 10, with and without aftertreatment).

Results
1. Assess the fastnesses to light and washing of the three dyeings using the blue scale and grey scales respectively. Note the effect of the aftertreatment on (a) the colour and (b) the light and wash fastnesses of C.I. Leuco Sulphur Brown 10.
2. Students of dye chemistry should consult the *Colour Index* for information on the structure of the two dyes used and, more importantly, how they are produced.

4.8 AZOIC DYES
The azoic dye system differs from those described previously in two important respects: (a) the colouring matter is a water-insoluble pigment and (b) it is formed in the fibre after separate treatment of the fibre with two water-soluble components. Thus the fibre is first impregnated with a coupling component, usually an alkaline solution of a derivative of 3-hydroxy-2-naphthoic acid, then subsequently treated with a solution of the diazo component, a diazonium salt of an aromatic base.

The azoic dyes are unique in that the dyer selects the combination of coupling component and diazo component that will give a dyeing of the required hue and fastness properties. There are about 35 coupling components and 50 diazo components commercially available. In principle any coupling component–diazo component combination can be used, but in practice the choice is limited to a relatively few combinations, and, of the range of colours obtainable, reds, oranges and maroons predominate, along with a selection of yellows, browns and blue-violet shades. The fastness to light and wet treatments of azoic dyes on cellulosic fibres is of a high standard, and they provide the most saturated shades within their colour gamut of all dye classes. As a result of this and the dyes' economic attractions, the consumption of azoic dyes on cellulosic fibres is still significant, representing about 8% of total dye consumption.

The following experiment illustrates the method of producing azoic dyeings, the variations in hue that can be obtained and the importance of an adequate soaping treatment after dyeing.

Procedure[1]
1. To dissolve the coupling agent paste 3.6 g C.I. Azoic Coupling Component 2 with a little

---

1. Rubber gloves should be worn to prevent staining of the hands. In the experiment seven different diazo components are used with the same coupling component.

wetting agent and hot water (60°C). Add 10 ml sodium hydroxide (10%) solution, 170 ml boiling water and 18 g common salt. The solution should then be a clear yellow. Make up the solution to 700 ml with hot water, ensuring that the final solution is still clear.

2. Treat eight 10 g skeins of cotton in the solution prepared in 1. at about 70°C and continue the treatment for 30 min in a cooling bath. This treatment is sometimes called 'naphtholation'.

3. Remove the skeins and squeeze well without rinsing. Separate the skeins and prepare for immersion into seven separate diazo solutions previously prepared as indicated in 4. below. Material impregnated with coupling components must be carefully protected from water spots, steam, acid fumes, chlorine fumes and direct sunlight before treatment with the diazonium compound. Failure to do so may result in weak or uneven dyeings. This effect can be illustrated by exposing the eighth impregnated skein at a window for 2 h before adding to one of the C.I. Azoic Diazo Component 6 solutions.

4. The diazo components are sold as (a) 'bases', which require diazotisation (with hydrochloric acid and sodium nitrite) before use or (b) stabilised 'salts', which require only the addition of water to render them suitable for use. Prepare as follows the seven C.I. Azoic Diazo Components 1, 5, 6, 20, 32, 41 and 46. Prepare two solutions for C.I. Azoic Diazo Component 6.

    Either (a) Weigh out 0.25 g of base, add 2 ml of hydrochloric acid (conc.), paste well, add 3 ml sodium nitrite solution (10%), stir well and then add 50 ml water and ice; allow to stand for 5 min. Finally add sodium acetate until Congo red paper changes from blue to red. This should ensure a pH in the range 4–5 and a volume of 100 ml.

    Or (b) Use the stabilised diazo salts. Weigh 1.0 g of the salt, add a few ml of methylated spirits, paste well and then add 10 ml water (40°C). Stir for 5 min, dilute to 100 ml with cold water containing 25 g/l common salt.

    In large-scale practice the amount of acid used in the diazotisation varies, depending on the strength of the aromatic base used as diazo component. The conditions given here represent average amounts of hydrochloric acid and sodium nitrite.

5. Add one skein impregnated with the coupling component into each of the seven diazo components, keeping the temperature below 10°C. Treat for 10 min in the diazo solution. Add the skein which has been exposed at the window to the second diazo solution of C.I. Diazo Component 6.

6. One common difficulty encountered with azoic dyes is that of ensuring that dyeings do not stain adjacent white material on rubbing because of pigment particles deposited externally on the fibres. In practice, to minimise this fault in the final dyeing, all stages of the application procedure should be performed so that subsequent formation of the azoic dye takes place deep in the individual fibres. Thus, for example, a coupling component of high substantivity should be used; salt should be added to the bath to improve exhaustion; naphtholation should be begun hot (80°C) and continued in a cooling bath; and the naphtholated fibre should either be dried or rinsed in salt solution before development. To confirm that coupling is complete, patterns may be examined in the dark under an ultra-violet lamp, together with an uncoupled pattern impregnated with the same coupling component. Uncoupled coupling component should be evident from its characteristic fluorescence.

In order to achieve optimum fastness to wet treatments, it is also necessary to give at least one final soaping treatment to the dyeings. This is achieved by boiling in a 2 g/l solution of soap or synthetic detergent (non-ionic) for 15 min. An indication of the amount of loose azoic pigment attached to the surface of the fibre can be obtained by carrying out repeated soapings (up to five times) for any one of the dyeings.

Results
1. Note the range of hues obtained with the seven azoic combinations based on the same coupling component.
2. Compare the two dyeings using C.I. Azoic Diazo Component 6, and comment on the effect produced by light on the skein exposed at the window before coupling.
3. Qualitatively note the effect of repeated soapings on the rubbing fastness of the final dyeings.
4. As mentioned in item 3. of the procedure, naphtholated material is sensitive to agencies such as light, atmospheric carbon dioxide and acid steam, when conversion of the soluble naphtholate to the insoluble naphthol may occur. In practice formaldehyde is often added to the naphtholating bath to prevent this. Students of organic chemistry should attempt to explain the action of the formaldehyde in this situation.
5. If desired, the fastness of the azoic dyes to washing at 95°C can be tested by carrying out the ISO 4 wash fastness test.
6. Explain why it is desirable to allow the bath to cool during naphtholation (see item 2. of the procedure).

4.9 PHTHALOGEN DYES
The discovery of the phthalocyanine pigments by Scottish Dyes Ltd (now ICI) at Grangemouth in 1928 must rank as one of the outstanding events in colour chemistry of the century. Copper phthalocyanine provides almost all the blue organic pigments in use today, combining brilliance and strength of shade with outstanding fastness properties, and it is not surprising that many attempts have been made to exploit the phthalocyanine nucleus in dyestuff chemistry. The introduction of sulphonic acid groups gives direct dyes for cotton or acid dyes for wool depending on the degree of sulphonation. Thus C.I. Direct Blue 86 retains the brilliant greenish-blue of copper phthalocyanine but has poor wet fastness and inferior light fastness to the parent compound. Sulphonated phthalocyanines also aggregate strongly in the presence of electrolytes.

The introduction of temporary solubility in the shape of quarternary groups formed the basis of the Alcian (ICI) range of dyes based on copper phthalocyanine. After application under mildly acid conditions the quaternary group was subsequently removed by an alkaline treatment. Alcian dyes are no longer marketed. The most ingenious method to produce a dye based on copper phthalocyanine was developed by Bayer in the Phthalogen range of dyes, where the blue pigment is synthesised *in situ* using the reactive 1-amino-3-imino-isoindolenine as a low molecular weight intermediate. There are two groups of these dyes:
(a) Phthalogen M brands, which are mixtures of the reactive intermediate and a metal compound developed on the textile material by the action of heat
(b) Phthalogen K brands, which are pre-polymers present as metal complexes, and are usually given an alkaline reduction development.

The Phthalogen dyes are classified as ingrain dyes in the *Colour Index*, although only a few members of the range are now marketed.

In the following experiment the hue and fastness properties of a Phthalogen K dye are compared with those of a direct dye obtained by sulphonation of copper phthalocyanine.

Procedure
Use a 5 g sample of wetted out white cotton to prepare a dyeing of C.I. Ingrain Blue 13 (Phthalogen Brilliant Blue IF3GK).

1. The affinity of Phthalogen K dyes is promoted if the cotton is pre-mordanted in the presence of sodium sulphate (Glauber's salt). Treat the cotton in a bath containing Phthalofix FN (1%) and Glauber's salt (20 g/l) at a temperature of 80°C and a liquor ratio of 50:1. Paste the Phthalofix FN (the mordanting agent) with a little warm water. Add about 80 ml hot (80°C) water and stir until a solution is obtained. Add this solution to about 170 ml water at 80°C. Treat the material in this bath for 10 min and over the next 15 min add the Glauber's salt in portions. Continue the treatment for a further 15 min at 80°C. Remove the sample and rinse in 250 ml of cold water, ensuring that it is cool after this treatment.

2. The dyeing is carried out using Phthalogen Brilliant Blue IF3GK (2%) at about pH 4 and at ambient temperature. Using a dry beaker, the dye is first pasted by stirring with 4% Levasol DG. Then add 10% glacial acid (do not use more dilute solutions) and allow to stand. All traces of water must be avoided. This concentrated solution remains stable for about 2 h. Prepare the dyebath by adding sufficient acetic acid to 250 ml cold water to give a pH of about 4.0. Treat the rinsed cotton in this for 5 min before adding the dissolved dye. Dye in the cold bath for 30 min and rinse in cold water, when the cotton should be a yellow-green colour.

3. The copper phthalocyanine is generated *in situ* by an alkaline reduction treatment using sodium hydroxide (30%) (1.2 ml) and sodium dithionite (0.5 g) at a liquor ratio of 50:1. Treat the cotton for 10 min at 75°C and for a further 10 min at 85°C.

4. Treat the dyed cotton for 10 min at 50°C in a beaker containing 1 ml conc. HCl and 250 ml water. Finally soap the dyeing at 95°C in a solution of non-ionic detergent (1 g/l) and soda ash (1 g/l). Rinse in cold water.

5. For comparison, dye a 5 g piece of white cotton using C.I. Direct Blue 86 (3%) and Glauber's salt (30%) at a liquor ratio of 50:1. Begin dyeing at 50°C, raise the temperature to the boil, during which time make the addition of electrolyte. Dye at the boil for a further 30 min. Rinse in cold water.

6. Carry out wash fastness tests on a portion of each dyeing using the ISO 4 (95°C) test. Mount a portion of each dyeing along with the light (blue wool) standards. After at least 60 h exposure in a light fading lamp, remove the samples.

Results

1. Compare the two dyeings visually for hue and if possible with a sample of copper phthalocyanine pigment (e.g. in a paint sample or printed ink).

2. Compare and record the fastnesses to light of the Phthalogen and direct dyeings using the blue wool scale, and to washing (ISO 4) using the grey scales.

3. Students of organic chemistry should find out the structure of 1-amino-3-imino-isoindolenine and note its relationship with the phthalocyanine molecule.

4.10 REACTIVE DYES

The first ranges of these dyes, the Procion MX (ICI) and Cibacron (CGY) dyes, were introduced in 1956 and were followed by the Procion H, Remazol (HOE), Levafix (BAY), Primazin (BASF), Drimarene (S) and other ranges. An essential feature of every member of each of these groups of dyes is the presence within the molecules of an atom or group that can react covalently with the hydroxyl, or more strictly the ionised hydroxyl, groups in the cellulose molecule. The chemistry of reactive dyes is fully discussed in section 9.2.

The first reactive dyes were developed specifically for continuous processing (or printing) by linking together in the dye molecule a chromophoric block in the form of a dye with low affinity for cellulose (e.g. an acid wool dye) and a reactive group capable of forming, under alkaline conditions, a covalent bond with cellulose through its hydroxyl groups. Thus, in principle, it was possible to combine both the brightness of shade and levelness from the acid dye chromophore with the optimum wet fastness afforded by the covalent linkage through the reactive group. All major dye manufacturers now market ranges of reactive dyes for cellulosic fibres based on the above principles. Many variations have been introduced since the appearance of the original three Procion dyes, including ranges of dyes of high reactivity and high exhaustion for batch application, and dyes reacting with the fibre under neutral conditions.

Reactive dyes may be applied using batch exhaustion, semi-continuous and continuous methods, and by printing techniques. They are, in terms of worldwide consumption, one of the important classes of dyes for cellulosics, comprising about 10% of the total consumption of dyes on these fibres. Compared with other dye classes, reactive dyes are important both in printing and in dyeing, though in absolute terms about twice the quantity is used for dyeing than is used in printing.

In the dyeing of cellulose with reactive dyes, the dye–fibre reaction is almost always promoted by alkaline conditions, as is also the reaction of the dye with water (hydrolysis), which gives a non-reactive and fugitive dye. The efficiency of the dyeing process is increased by promoting dye–fibre combination and suppressing the reaction with water. Indeed, the wet fastness of the dyeings depends on this. The development of maximum fastness to wet treatments, however, is also dependent on the completeness of the removal from the fibre of dye not chemically bound to it. In addition, the dyed cotton is sensitive to acid hydrolysis after the dye has reacted with the fibre and this results in breaking of the dye–fibre bond and, in pale dyeings, of inferior wet fastness.

The following experiment uses two typical types of reactive dye, cold-dyeing and hot-dyeing, and illustrates some of the features of the reactive dye–cellulose system. Although developments in reactive dye chemistry (see section 9.2) have meant that some dyes of the types used in this experiment have been superseded by dyes with specialised properties such as high degrees of exhaustion, the principles illustrated apply to all reactive dyes.

Procedure
1. Prepare dyebaths as shown in Table 4.7, using 10 g pieces of cotton for each dyebath.
   (a) For C.I. Reactive Red 1 carry out two dyeings at 40°C and one at 75°C for 30 min, adding the electrolyte after 10 min. For C.I. Reactive Blue 3 carry out two dyeings at 75°C and one at 40°C for 30 min, again adding the electrolyte after 10 min. Soap one of the 40°C dyeings and the 75°C dyeing of C.I. Reactive Red 1 (I and III), and one of the 75°C dyeings and the 40°C dyeing of C.I. Reactive Blue 3 (IV and VI) in a solution of 2 g/l of a non-ionic detergent at the boil. Rinse these four dyeings and dry along with the 'unsoaped' dyeings of the two dyes.
   (b) Carry out hot pressing tests on half (5 g) of the soaped and unsoaped dyeings at 40°C of C.I. Reactive Red 1 (I and II) and C.I. Reactive Blue 3 at 75°C (IV and V) by placing each dyed pattern between two pieces of moistened white fabric and pressing with a hot iron.
2. (a) To examine the behaviour of the 'hydrolysed' dyes prepare two dyebaths as for dyeings I and IV above. Before entering the patterns, heat these dyebaths to boiling and boil gently for 15 min. Cool to the appropriate dyeing temperature and dye a 5 g piece of cotton in each 'hydrolysed' dyebath as above. After 30 min dyeing remove the patterns.
   (b) After dyeing acidify the C.I. Reactive Red 1 dyebath to give a pH of 2–3 and insert

TABLE 4.7

	Amount (% o.w.f.)					
	I[a]	II[a]	III[b]	IV[b]	V[b]	VI[a]
C.I. Reactive Red 1	2	2	2			
C.I. Reactive Blue 3				2	2	2
Glauber's salt (g/l)	50	50	50	50	50	50
Sodium carbonate (g/l)	10	10	10	10	10	10

Liquor ratio 30:1
Temperature (°C): (a) 40
               (b) 75

  a small sample of wool and dye for 10 min.
3. To illustrate the effect of acid hydrolysis on reactive dyed cellulose, treat a 2.5 g portion of the soaped dyeing of C.I. Reactive Red 1 (dyeing I) with 1 g/l Matexil FC-PRP (ICI) and 1 g/l of a non-ionic detergent for 15 min cold. Then treat half a further 2.5 g portion of dyeing I and the dyeing treated with Matexil FC-PRP separately in a 1 g/l solution of acetic acid for 30 min at the boil at a liquor ratio of 50:1.
4. The basis of the various continuous procedures available is the impregnation of the material with a solution of reactive dye (in the presence or absence of alkali), drying, padding with alkali (if alkali was not added initially) and then fixing the dye by some means to promote dye–fibre reaction. The simplest way to achieve this fixation is by the semi-continuous pad–batch method using cold-dyeing reactive dyes, where fixation is achieved simply by batching the padded fabric and leaving for a number of hours at room temperature. Dye manufacturers offer ranges of dyes designed for continuous application. This part of the experiment attempts to illustrate the pad–batch process.
  Prepare the dyeings by impregnating pieces of bleached cotton with the recipe given in Table 4.8. Remove excess liquor by squeezing or passage through a mangle. Roll up both pieces, place in stoppered test tubes and leave overnight. Wash in cold running water after removal from the test tubes and treat both dyeings in 2 g/l soap for 15 min

TABLE 4.8

	Concn (g/l)	
	I	II
C.I. Reactive Red 1	50	50
Urea	100	100
Sodium carbonate	50	

at 50°C. Dry the samples. Though a continuous or semi-continuous dyeing range is desirable for such dyeing procedures, this experiment attempts to illustrate the way in which highly reactive dyes can be 'fixed' by the presence of alkali even at room temperature.

Results

1. (a) Compare and comment on the depths of shade obtained from the two soaped dyeings (40°C and 75°C) of C.I. Reactive Red 1 and the two soaped dyeings (40°C and 75°C) of C.I. Reactive Blue 3.

   (b) Compare the staining of the hot damp pressing tests for the soaped and unsoaped dyeings. This illustrates the importance of removing unfixed dye after dyeing.

2. For C.I. Reactive Red 1 and C.I. Reactive Blue 3, compare the shades of the soaped dyeings (40°C for C.I. Reactive Red 1 and 75°C for C.I. Reactive Blue 3) and the hydrolysed dyeings. This comparison gives a measure of the relative reactivities of the cold and hot dyeing reactive dyes. From the results, suggest which dye has the more reactive system. If the *Colour Index* is available, compare the structure of C.I. Reactive Red 1 (C.I. 18158) with that of C.I. Acid Red 1 (C.I. 18050) and hence account for the dyeing obtained by inserting a piece of wool into the acidified dyebath in item 2(b) of the procedure.

3. Note the effect of hydrolysis of 'fixed' dye under acidic conditions by comparing the 'treated' and 'untreated' dyeings of C.I. Reactive Red 1. Comment on the effect on acid hydrolysis of Matexil FC-PRP (ICI), which is an aqueous solution of organic amines and is quite alkaline.

4. Compare the final shades of the two dyeings from the pad–batch technique and comment on the results.

5. Students of dye chemistry should familiarise themselves with the reactive systems used in the two dyes and discuss the relative reactivities bearing in mind the results obtained in item 2(a) of the procedure.

REFERENCE

1. 'The dyeing of cellulosic fibres', Ed. C Preston (Bradford: Dyers' Company Publications Trust, 1985).

5 DYES FOR SYNTHETIC FIBRES

5.1 DISPERSE DYES ON SYNTHETIC FIBRES

When the first commercial synthetic fibre (secondary cellulose acetate) was introduced in about 1920, none of the existing classes of dye was capable of dyeing it satisfactorily. During the next few years it was found that aminoazobenzene and aminoanthraquinone compounds, when applied from an aqueous dispersion in the presence of a surface-active dispersing agent, gave a range of level shades of adequate fastness on the new fibre. Such compounds still form the basis of the ranges of disperse dyes currently available for the dyeing of a number of synthetic fibres. The aminoazobenzenes provide mainly yellow, orange and red dyes, though the recent use of heterocyclic diazo components has extended this range to include violets and even blues. Aminoanthraquinone derivatives, which are more expensive than the aminoazobenzenes, give mainly bright reds, blues and violets, with a few bluish-greens (see also section 9.3).

As shown in the experiment described in this section, disperse dyes can be used for the coloration of all the important synthetic fibres. In practice, however, their use is restricted to the dyeing of the cellulose acetates and polyesters, and nylon is primarily dyed with acid and metal-complex acid dyes, while basic dyes are used almost exclusively for dyeing acrylic fibres. Thus, although disperse dyes give more level dyeings on nylon than do acid dyes, their fastness to wet treatments on that fibre does not meet normal requirements. On acrylic fibres the build-up of disperse dyes is poor and their use on this fibre is therefore restricted to pale shades.

Since the publication of the third edition of the *Colour Index* there has been a significant increase in the number of available disperse dyes, this in a period when many dyes classes were showing a decrease. Most of these new dyes were designed specifically for use on polyester and its blends.

Disperse dyes, which have a low aqueous solubility due to their lack of ionic groups, show different degrees of substantivity on different fibres. Where the rate of dyeing is low, e.g. in polyester dyeing, this may be improved by the use of high temperatures (120 or 130°C) and/or auxiliary agents (carriers). A given disperse dye may show wide differences in exhaustion, fastness to wet treatments and light, and even hue when applied to different fibres. The following experiment illustrates some of these effects.

Procedure

Using 2 g pieces of the following fabrics, produce three dyeings on each as detailed in Table 5.1, dyeing for 45 min. Rinse in cold water and dry:
(a) Secondary cellulose acetate
(b) Cellulose triacetate
(c) Nylon 6.6
(d) Nylon 6 (optional)
(e) Acrylic (e.g. Courtelle)
(f) Polyester (e.g. Terylene).

TABLE 5.1

	Amount (% o.w.f.)		
	I[a]	II[b]	III[c]
C.I. Disperse Red 11	2	2	2
Non-ionic dispersing agent (e.g. Matexil DN-VL (ICI) (g/l)	1	1	1

Temperature (°C):   (a) 60
 (b) 75
 (c) 95

Liquor ratio 50:1

Results
1. Examine and comment on the relative uptakes of the disperse dye by the various fibres.
2. Examine the effect of temperature on the uptake of dye by the fibres and suggest any reasons for the observed effects.
3. Compare the hues of the six dyed fabrics, particularly the cellulose acetates on the one hand and the nylons on the other. In common with a number of disperse dyes, C.I. Disperse Red 11 stains or dyes wool. Suggest the likeliest hue of the dyeing of wool and check your suggestion by carrying out a small-scale dyeing in a test tube using a small piece of wool.
4. From the *Colour Index* establish to which of the chemical types mentioned in the introduction C.I. Disperse Red 11 belongs.
5. The aminoazobenzene disperse dyes have the general formula shown in Figure 5.1. Students of dye chemistry should indicate the nature (electron withdrawing or electron donating) of groups R_1 to R_7, and attempt to explain how colour results from such structures.

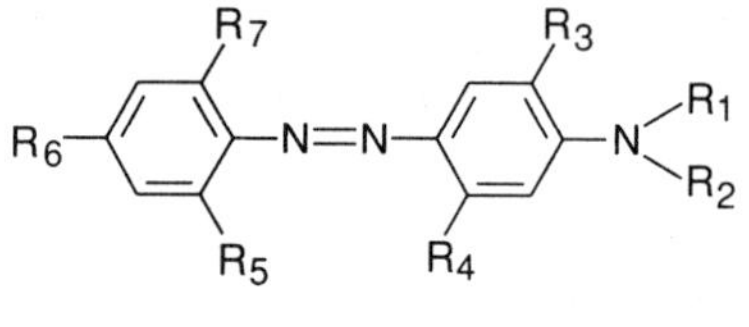

Figure 5.1 – General formula of aminoazobenzene disperse dyes

5.2 THE DYEING OF CELLULOSE ACETATE (SECONDARY ACETATE)
The hydroxyl groups in cellulose allow the fibre to be esterified, but although esters of cellulose have been known for over a hundred years it was not until 1921 that the large-scale manufacture of the first commercial cellulose acetate fibre was begun. This was called Celanese and the fibre is now generically known as secondary cellulose acetate (Dicel). It is obtained by the partial hydrolysis of fully acetylated cellulose until an average 2.3–2.5 of the three original hydroxyl groups per anhydroglucose unit remain acetylated. Secon-

dary cellulose acetate differs in physical properties and in dyeing properties from the fully acetylated cellulose triacetate (Tricel), being more hydrophilic, weaker and less resistant to thermal treatments than the latter, and is used mainly in dress, lining, furnishing and lingerie fabrics.

Secondary cellulose acetate is dyed exclusively with disperse dyes. The dyeing behaviour of these dyes on secondary cellulose acetate does, however, vary from one dye to another, particularly with respect to their rate of uptake by the fibre and to what extent the uptake is governed by temperature. The following experiments, which are based on the SDC report on the dyeing properties of disperse dyes, examine firstly the temperature range properties and secondly the rates of dyeing of two disperse dyes and their mixture.

Procedure (a)
Prepare five dyebaths for each of the conditions I, II and III as shown in Table 5.2, for use with 2 g pieces of cellulose acetate fabric. Carry out dyeings I, II and III for 1 h each at temperatures of 50, 60, 70, 80 and 90°C. Rinse and dry samples. The temperature range properties are assessed as follows using the grey scales.

If the dyeing at 50°C is almost equal in depth to that at 90°C, i.e. if the assessment of the grey scale contrast is not below 4–5, the temperature range properties are rated as 'excellent' (A). If the dyeing at 60°C has to be used for comparison with that at 90°C to achieve this small degree of contrast, the rating is 'very good' (B). Similarly choice of the 70°C dyeing indicates a rating of 'good' (C), and a choice of the 80°C dyeing a rating of 'moderate' (D). If the 80 and 90°C dyeings show a considerable contrast, i.e. a grey scale contrast below 4–5, the rating is 'poor' (E).

TABLE 5.2

| | Amount (% o.w.f.) | | |
	I	II	III
C.I. Disperse Red 1	2		1
C.I. Disperse Blue 83		2	1
Non-ionic dispersing agent (g/l)	1	1	1

Liquor ratio 50:1

Results
1. Classify the two dyes on the A–E scale for temperature range properties.
2. Comment on the suitability of the two dyes in admixture.

Procedure (b)
Prepare a second set of dyebaths as shown in Table 5.2 for each of the two dyes and also for the mixture, for use with 2 g pieces of cellulose acetate fabric. Dyeing times should be for 5, 15, 30, 60 and 120 min, all at 80°C. Rinse and dry. The rate of dyeing properties are

assessed by determining the ratings on the grey scale for assessing change in colour contrasts between dyeings carried out for:

(a) 120 and 5 min: if not below grey scale rating 4–5, report as very rapid dyeing (A), otherwise
(b) 120 and 15 min: if not below grey scale rating 4–5 report as rapid dyeing (B), otherwise
(c) 120 and 30 min: if not below grey scale rating 4–5 report as moderate dyeing (C), otherwise
(d) 120 and 60 min: if not below grey scale rating 4–5, report as slow dyeing (D), otherwise
(e) Report as very slow dyeing (E).

Results
1. Classify the two dyes on the A–E scale according to their rate of dyeing properties.
2. If the *Colour Index* is available, check the chemical classes to which C.I. Disperse Red 1 and C.I. Disperse Blue 83 belong, and comment on any relationship between the structures of the two dyes, and their dyeing properties as shown by the mixture dyeings III.
3. Comment on the practical problems associated with the jig dyeing of cellulose acetate with mixtures of disperse dyes.

5.3 DISPERSE DYES ON POLYESTER (CARRIER DYEING)

Though a number of different types of polyester is commercially available, the most important as textile fibres are those produced from poly(ethylene terephthalate). These give strong fibres in both filament and staple form and make polyester suitable for extensive blending with cotton in shirting fabrics. Bulked filament yarns are also blended in large amounts with wool for suiting materials.

Disperse dyes are used almost exclusively for the dyeing of polyester fibres though they vary widely in rate of dyeing, fastness properties and sensitivity to oligomers, which are low molecular weight (usually trimeric) compounds associated with the high molecular weight fibrous polymer; during dyeing these provide nuclei for crystallisation of the dyes. Classifications of disperse dyes into groups of similar properties have been made and one such system divides the dyes into four groups based on a relationship between their dyeing properties and their fastness to the treatments required for many end uses. Thus class A includes most of the lower molecular weight dyes which, though having high rates of diffusion in the fibre, have poor heat fastness. At the other end of the scale, class D dyes are those of higher molecular weight, slow rates of diffusion and excellent fastness properties. Dyes in classes B and C have intermediate properties. The SDC committee on the dyeing properties of disperse dyes has published test methods for the build up, migration, diffusion in high-temperature dyeing and critical temperature (that which gives 50% exhaustion in 20 min) for polyester dyeing.

As seen in the experiment in section 5.1, the build-up of disperse dyes on polyester at temperatures up to 95°C is generally poor, owing to a low rate of dye penetration into the fibre at these temperatures. This rate can be increased by:
(a) The use of carriers (class B and C dyes)
(b) Dyeing at higher temperatures.

The types of carrier in use commercially are based on compounds like biphenyl, substituted phenols, chlorinated aromatic hydrocarbons and alkylnaphthalenes, and all traces of these must be removed from the polyester after dyeing because of their odour and possible adverse effects on the light fastness of the dyes.

Carrier dyeing and high-temperature dyeing are used in the application of disperse dyes to cellulose triacetate for the same reasons. The following experiment illustrates the effect of increasing amounts of carrier on the dyeing of polyester at the boil.

Procedure
For five 5 g skeins of polyester yarn or 2.5 g pieces of polyester fabric, prepare the dyebaths shown in Table 5.3. Start the dyeings at 50°C, raise the temperature to the boil and dye for 1 h at this temperature. Rinse. Then soap the dyeings in a bath containing 2 g/l non-ionic detergent and 0.5 g/l sodium carbonate for 15 min at 75°C.

TABLE 5.3

	Amount (% o.w.f.)				
	I	II	III	IV	V
C.I. Disperse Violet 33	1	1	1	1	1
Carrier (Matexil CA-MN (ICI) (g/l)		1	2	4	6

Liquor ratio 40:1

Results
1. Comment on the effect of increasing amounts of carrier on the depth of shade.
2. Try to assess visually the difference in depth of shade between dyeings I and IV. Check your estimate by carrying out a further dyeing (without carrier) to match dyeing IV.
3. Comment on any difference observed between dyeings IV and V.
4. C.I. Disperse Violet 33 is a class C dye. Explain which classes of dye would be most suitable for the following:
   (a) The batch dyeing of polyester/cotton blends
   (b) The batch dyeing of polyester/wool blends
   (c) The transfer printing of polyester fabric.

5.4 DISPERSE DYES ON POLYESTER (HIGH-TEMPERATURE (HT) DYEING))
As pointed out in the previous experiment, it is not easy to obtain full depths of shade on polyester at the boil (even with the use of carriers) due to the low rate of diffusion of disperse dyes into the fibre at 100°C. This is particularly so with class C and D dyes, but by raising the temperature to above 100°C this rate can be greatly increased and heavy dyeings may be obtained. Many modern disperse dyes have relatively high molecular weights and low rates of diffusion and therefore require these high temperatures for full-depth dyeings to be achieved.

The following experiment illustrates two features of polyester dyeing:
(a) The effect of temperature in the 100–130°C range on the depth of dyeing obtainable
(b) The value of the reduction clearing treatment (an alkaline reducing aftertreatment) which is recommended for optimum wet fastness and rub fastness properties, particularly in medium to heavy depths of shade.

This experiment requires the use of a laboratory high-temperature dyeing machine.

Procedure

1. Using either 10 g skeins of polyester yarn or 5 g pieces of fabric, prepare four dyebaths as shown in Table 5.4. The liquor ratio employed will depend on whether yarn or fabric is used and also on the available volume of the dye vessels for the high-temperature machine. Start the dyeings at about 70°C, raise the temperature to the required value and dye at this temperature for 30 min.
2. Reduction clearing is performed after dyeing. Split the sample from dyeing IV in two and treat one half at a liquor ratio of approx. 15:1 with sodium hydroxide (2 g/l), sodium dithionite (2 g/l) and dispersing agent (2 g/l). Enter the sample at 50°C, raise the temperature to 75°C and treat at this temperature for 20 min. Rinse and dry.
3. In order to assess the effect on fastness of the reduction clearing treatment, carry out washing tests at 95°C (ISO 4) on the treated and untreated samples from dyeing IV. Alternatively simple rub fastness tests can be carried out by rubbing two pieces of white cotton (preferably damp) held between the fingers against the dyeings. This is most easily done if yarn has been used for the dyeings.

TABLE 5.4

	Amount (% o.w.f.)			
	I[(a)]	II[(b)]	III[(c)]	IV[(d)]
C.I. Disperse Blue 122	5	5	5	5
Dispersing agent (g/l)	1	1	1	1

Temperature (°C):   (a) 100
                    (b) 110
                    (c) 120
                    (d) 130
Liquor ratio 15:1–30:1 (depending on dyeing equipment)

Results

1. The effect of temperature on the depth of dyeing can be assessed by use of the grey scales, taking the 130°C dyeing as grade 5 and comparing the others to it. Try to assess visually the difference in depth between dyeings II (or III) and IV and check this by carrying out a further dyeing at the lower temperature with additional dye in order to match the depth of the 130°C dyeing.
2. By means of the grey scale for assessing colour staining assess the effectiveness of the reduction clearing treatment on the wash and/or the rub fastness.
3. Explain why polyester fibres may be sensitive to high-temperature alkaline conditions and also why the reduction clearing treatment affects only surface dye.
4. Apart from the normal effect of heat in increasing the rate of chemical reactions, the marked change in uptake of disperse dyes by polyesters is influenced by a change in the properties of the non-crystalline regions of the fibre on heating. The temperature at

which this takes place is known as the second-order or glass transition temperature (T_g) and above this the dyeability of the fibre is greatly improved, due to increased accessibility of the non-crystalline regions to dye molecules. The T_g for polyester may vary from 80 to 130°C, and higher, depending on the crystallinity of the fibre. From an examination of dyeings I to IV, assess approximately the T_g of the polyester used (see also sections 8.6 and 9.5).

5.5 DISPERSE DYES ON POLYESTER (EFFECT OF HEAT SETTING)

Polyester yarn and fabric are often heat set before dyeing. The treatment consists essentially of exposing the material, often under tension, to a temperature approximately 30 degC above that likely to be encountered in its subsequent life. During heat setting the weak intermolecular bonds between the polymer chains are broken, and on cooling a rearrangement occurs resulting in a dimensionally more stable product. Unset polyester yarn shrinks by about 7% in boiling water, an effect which may cause problems in package dyeing, while for most purposes continuous filament fabrics require some heat treatment to confer dimensional stability. The dyeability of heat-set polyester is often affected by the treatment, which in practice may be carried out using steam or dry heat.

The following experiment illustrates the effect of dry heat on the uptake of a disperse dye by polyester yarn.

Procedure

1. Using an ordinary oven to simulate the conditions of heat setting, treat five 2.5 g skeins of polyester yarn, one at each of the following temperatures for 10 min: 120, 150, 210, 220 and 230°C.
2. Dye all five skeins along with an untreated skein in a dyebath containing C.I. Disperse Blue 7 (4%) and carrier (Matexil CA-MN (ICI)) (4 ml/l) at a liquor ratio of approx. 30:1. Enter the wetted out skeins at 70°C, raise the temperature to the boil and dye at this temperature for at least 45 min. Treat all the skeins for 30 min at 70–80°C in a solution of 2 g/l soap or detergent.

Results

1. By examining the heat-set dyeings determine the optimum temperature range for this treatment in order to give maximum depth of shade for C.I. Disperse Blue 7.
2. The uptake of disperse dyes on heat-set polyester depends not only on the temperature of setting but also on such factors as:
    (a) Dyeing method (carrier or high temperature)
    (b) Type of carrier
    (c) The tension applied to the polyester during setting.

Factor (a) can be checked by repeating the experiment using high-temperature dyeing conditions without any carrier.

5.6 MIXTURES OF ACID DYES ON NYLON

Nylon is at the same time one of the easiest and most difficult of the synthetic fibres to dye. Thus almost all classes of dye have substantivity for the fibre, but other factors such as fastness, chemical and physical variations in the fibre, levelness and economics restrict the choice considerably and no one class of dye completely satisfies all requirements. Acid dyes, which are the most widely used, give a wide range of hues and dyeings of suitable fastness, though they usually require an aftertreatment to confer adequate wet fastness. In addition, those dyes with the best fastness properties show only moderate to poor migration and coverage of fibre variations. The use of disperse dyes, which have better levelling properties, is restricted to very pale shades (e.g. on nylon hosiery) because of the inferior wet fastness properties associated with these dyes. A few selected direct dyes, where levelling and coverage properties are again only moderate, supplement the acid dye ranges. Other dye classes find only limited use, e.g. basic dyes for basic-dyeable nylon and a few sulphur and vat dyes for nylon/cotton blends.

Of the available acid dyes (see Chapter 3), the milling, neutral-dyeing, and metal-complex types are preferred for the dyeing of nylon, supplemented in certain cases by selected levelling dyes. These are applied to nylon under similar conditions as those described for wool in section 3.2 with the addition of levelling agents. Because of the limited number of amine groups compared with wool, nylon becomes saturated with anionic, e.g. acid, dyes at relatively low depths. Consequently, if full depths are produced by mixing two (or more) dyes of different degrees of sulphonation, one dye will be taken up preferentially. As the amount of all the dyes in the bath is increased, this particular dye will more and more dominate the final hue of the dyed material. The effect, sometimes known as blocking, is illustrated by the following experiment.

Procedure
Enter 2 g pieces of wool into baths I–IV and 2 g pieces of nylon into V–VIII (Table 5.5). Raise the temperature slowly and with stirring to 95–100°C and dye at this temperature for 30 min. With dyeings VII and VIII produce further dyeings using the exhausted dye solutions from the previous dyeings as follows:

Remove the first dyeing, returning as much as possible of the residual solution to the dye vessel. Cool by adding a little cold water and then enter a fresh pattern of undyed nylon. Raise the temperature quickly to the boil and dye at the boil for 15–20 min. It is essential for the fibre to be agitated continuously in the dye solution for the first few minutes in the bath. Repeat the process using the solution from the first exhaust dyeing.

Results
1. From the level of acidity of the dyebaths, indicate to what class the three acid dyes belong.
2. Explain any differences observed between pairs of dyeings I and V, II and VI, V and VI, VII and VIII. Relate these observations to any differences between the exhaust dyeings of VII and VIII.
3. C.I. Acid Yellow 17 is a disulphonated dye. Indicate which of the blue dyes is monosulphonated and which disulphonated. Check your answer from the structures given in the *Colour Index*.

5.7 BASIC DYES ON NATURAL AND SYNTHETIC FIBRES
Basic dyes were the earliest dyes commercially synthesised, starting with the discovery of mauveine by W H Perkin in 1856. They were characterised by brilliance of hue, high tinctorial strength and generally poor fastness to washing and light when applied to wool, silk and tannin-mordanted cotton. This mordanting pretreatment for cotton was devised by Perkin for his new product since the dye proved to have no substantivity for cotton and Perkin was advised that unless it could be used in the cotton trade it would not prove commercially attractive. Perkin's mordanting technique overcame the problem and forms the basis of current aftertreatments used to improve the wet fastness of acid dyes on nylon.

TABLE 5.5

	Amount (% o.w.f.)							
	I	II	III	IV	V	VI	VII	VIII
C.I. Acid Yellow 17	0.25	0.25	1.5	1.5	0.25	0.25	1.5	1.5
C.I. Acid Blue 45	0.167		1.0		0.167		1.0	
C.I. Acid Blue 47		0.167		1.0		0.167		1.0
Sulphuric acid (10%) (ml)	0.6	0.6	0.6	0.6				
Formic acid (1%) (ml)					1.7	1.7	1.7	1.7

Liquor ratio 50:1

With the advent of synthetic fibres based on polyacrylonitrile, it was found that basic dyes had good wash and moderate light fastness on these fibres, and now many new basic (cationic) dyes have been developed especially for acrylic fibres. The following experiment illustrates the dyeing of natural fibres (wool and cotton) as well as acrylic fibres with two of the original cationic dyes, and compares their fastness properties on the different substrates.

Procedure
1. (a) Pretreat a 5 g piece of cotton fabric by entering it into a bath containing 3% tannic acid and treat for 15 min at 50–60°C at a liquor ratio of 50:1. Remove, squeeze and treat in a second bath containing 1.5% tartar emetic (potassium antimony tartrate) for 15 min in the cold at a liquor ratio of 50:1. Rinse the sample.
   (b) Pretreat a 5 g piece of acrylic fabric for 15 min at 95°C in a bath containing 2% sodium acetate and 1% acetic acid.
   (c) Wet out a 5 g piece of wool fabric.
2. Prepare two dyebaths for each of the three fabrics as indicated in Table 5.6 using C.I. Basic Violet 1 and C.I. Basic Green 4. Start the dyeings at 40°C and raise the temperature to the required values.
3. (a) Carry out an ISO 2 wash test on each of the six dyed samples, using a liquor ratio of 50:1 in a 5 g/l soap solution for 45 min at 50°C. Sew the dyed cotton between undyed pieces of cotton and wool, the dyed acrylic between acrylic and wool or cotton and the dyed wool between wool and cotton.
   (b) Expose pieces of each dyed sample along with the blue wool standards either at a sunny window or under a suitable fading lamp.

Results
1. Use the grey scales to assess the fastness to washing at 50°C of the two dyes on each of the fibres.
2. Compare the relative fastness to light of the dyes on the different fibres.
3. Students of dye and fibre chemistry should explain the mechanisms by which wool and acrylic fibres are dyed using basic dyes.

TABLE 5.6

	Amount (% o.w.f.)		
	Cotton[a]	Acrylic[b]	Wool[c]
Dye	2	2	2
Sodium acetate		2	
Acetic acid	1	1	

	Temperature (°C)	Time at top temperature (min)
(a)	45	30
(b)	95	60
(c)	95	30

Liquor ratio 50:1

5.8 BASIC (CATIONIC) DYES ON ACRYLIC FIBRES

As seen in the experiment in section 5.1, disperse dyes will give only pale to medium depths on acrylic fibres and for most practical purposes basic (cationic) dyes must be used to produce a suitable range of dyeings on these fibres. Though the early basic dyes are suitable in this respect, they have been replaced by new ranges of basic dyes with improved fastness properties. One of the practical problems associated with the use of these dyes on acrylics is that they have very high strike when the dyebath temperature reaches the region between 75 and 85°C, though this is a function of the properties of the fibres rather than those of the dye. In order to minimise unlevelness due to high strike at these temperatures, restraining agents are added to the dyebath and the rate of temperature rise is carefully controlled. Alternatively rapid dyeing methods, in which dyeing is started above 85°C, may be used. Basic dyes build up very well to give deep dyeings of good wet fastness and usually good light fastness.

The experiment described below illustrates how the uptake of a typical basic dye on acrylic fibres is sensitive to dyebath temperature.

Procedure

1. Treat four 5 g skeins of acrylic yarn or 5 g pieces of an acrylic fabric in a bath containing acetic acid (1%) and sodium acetate (1%) Carry out the treatment for 15 min at 95°C at a liquor ratio of 50:1. Separate the skeins or pieces and squeeze to remove excess liquor.
2. Prepare four dyebaths as shown in Table 5.7. Enter one pretreated skein or piece into each dyebath set at the prescribed temperature. Dye at these temperatures for 75 min. Rinse in warm water and dry.

Results

1. Note the effect of temperature on the uptake of the basic dye and explain why basic (rather than anionic) dyes are used to dye most types of acrylic fibre.
2. Try to find out the particular physical property of acrylic fibres that gives rise to this temperature effect. The experiment described in section 8.6 deals with this property,

TABLE 5.7

	Amount (% o.w.f.)			
	I[a]	II[b]	III[c]	IV[d]
C.I. Basic Violet 7	2	2	2	2
Acetic acid (glacial)	1	1	1	1
Sodium acetate	2	2	2	2

Temperature (°C): (a) 60
                (b) 70
                (c) 80
                (d) 90
Liquor ratio 30:1–50:1

    which is common to all synthetic polymer fibres.
3. Examine dyeings II and III for evidence of unlevelness, though the effect is of course much more noticeable in bulk working.
4. Explain why dyed acrylics would not in practice receive a cold rinse after dyeing.

5.9 THE COMPATIBILITY OF BASIC DYES IN THE DYEING OF ACRYLIC FIBRES

Because of marked differences in the rates at which basic dyes are taken up by acrylic fibres during dyeing (particularly above 75°C and as seen in the previous experiment), coupled with low migration, it is desirable when applying dyes in admixture that these should be compatible. With this in mind, dyestuff manufacturers include in their technical data indices of compatibility for each range of dyes. The following experiment is a modification of the scheme suggested by the SDC for assigning an index to any basic dye, the dyeing behaviour of which is not known. The scheme uses five indices or K values of 1 to 5. In the experiment only three of the blue standards (K_1, K_2 and K_5) are used. The higher the K value assigned to a dye, the lower the dyeing rate.

Procedure

1. Prepare 36 1 g skeins of acrylic yarn by treating with acetic acid (glacial) (1%) and sodium acetate (2%) at a temperature of 95°C and liquor ratio 40:1–50:1. After 15 min allow the yarn to cool slowly. Squeeze, but do not dry.
2. The three blue (standard) dyes used in the experiment and their K values are given in Table 5.8. Using C.I. Basic Orange 42 and C.I. Basic Yellow 11 as dyes of unknown dyeing behaviour, prepare six dyebaths as shown in Table 5.9.
3. Using six damp pretreated skeins for each dyebath proceed as follows:
   (a) Enter the first skein and dye for 5 min for dyeings I and IV and 10 min for dyeings II, III, V and VI. Remove the skein, squeezing excess liquor into the dyebath, rinse and dry.

TABLE 5.8

Dye	K value
C.I. Basic Blue 69	1
C.I. Basic Blue 45	2
C.I. Basic Blue 22	5

TABLE 5.9

	Amount (% o.w.f.)					
	I	II	III	IV	V	VI
C.I. Basic Orange 42	0.55	0.55	0.55			
C.I. Basic Yellow 11				0.55	0.55	0.55
C.I. Basic Blue 69	0.55			0.55		
C.I. Basic Blue 45		2.7			2.7	
C.I. Basic Blue 22			2.4			2.4
Acetic acid (glacial)	1	1	1	1	1	1
Sodium acetate	1	1	1	1	1	1

Temperature 95°C
pH of dyebaths 4.3–4.7
Liquor ratio approx. 40:1

(b) Enter the second skeins into the same dyebath and dye for a similar time. Squeeze, rinse and dry and repeat the procedure until all six skeins have been dyed for each of the six dyebaths. If exhaustion has occurred before completion of the sequence, dyeing is stopped at that stage.

(c) Link together the six dyed skeins from each dyebath.

Results

1. By examination of the six sets of dyeings, assign a K value or compatibility index to C.I. Basic Orange 42 and C.I. Basic Yellow 11 based on the known values for the three blue dyes.
2. Students should refer to the more detailed test (J.S.D.C., **88** (1972) 220) and comment on the limitations of the test as indicated in section 7 therein.

6 DYEING OF FIBRE BLENDS

The term 'fibre blend' refers here to any yarn or fabric containing more than one type of fibre, though strictly speaking a 'blend' should refer to material in which the different fibres are spun together in the yarn. Very often natural fibres are used in blends along with synthetic fibres so that the aesthetic properties (e.g. handle, heat retention) of the former can be combined with the greater strength and durability of the latter. From the many combinations of different fibres, relatively few are of commercial importance in the textile industry and the experiments in this section illustrate some typical procedures for three of the most important of such fibre blends. The principles involved in the dyeing of these can be adapted for other blends.

Thus two fibres in a blend may or may not be dyeable with the same class of dye, though even if they are it is probable that a given dye will be taken up preferentially by one of the components. Sometimes a different class of dye will be required for each component of the blend and in principle such combinations of dye classes may be applied by either a one-bath or a multi-bath technique. Considerations such as dye compatibility, fastness requirements and cross-staining will determine whether a one-bath method is suitable, and, if not, the order in which the fibre components must by dyed.

The subject is further complicated by the fact that any one of four different dyed effects may be required:
(a) A solid dyeing, in which the same tone and depth are required on each fibre component
(b) A reserve effect, where one fibre should remain undyed
(c) A tone-in-tone effect, where different depths of the same hue are required
(d) A cross-dyeing, in which a contrasting hue is produced on the different fibres.

It should be apparent, even from the few examples considered here, that the dyeing of each fibre blend presents special difficulties. For a full discussion on the dyeing of blends, students should consult the literature [1,2].

6.1 ACID DYES ON A WOOL/NYLON MIXTURE
Blends of wool and nylon are important commercial materials with a variety of applications. In carpeting, for example, wool is often used in a blend with 20% nylon to improve the wearing properties.

Because of chemical similarities between wool and nylon, acid dyes may be used to dye both fibres, though for solid colours careful selection of dyes and of dyeing conditions is necessary. This is particularly so with sportswear and leisurewear fabrics and when mixtures of dyes are used, because, if the individual components of the mixture do not distribute themselves in the same proportions between the two fibres, these will be different in hue and the resulting two-tone effect will be much more objectionable to the eye than would a difference in depth of colour alone. Most levelling acid dyes colour the nylon preferentially in pale dyeings, but as the depth is increased the proportion of dye taken up by the wool increases, until a solid colour is obtained. The amount required to obtain this effect varies according to the nature of the dye.

As the depth is further increased the nylon becomes saturated and the colour continues to build up only on the wool. Blocking effects (see the experiment described in section 5.6) may also occur on the nylon if mixtures of dyes of different degrees of sulphonation are used.

Acid dyes may be applied from weakly acid baths although it is not usually advisable to employ sulphuric acid, because there is a risk of its causing tendering of the nylon, especially during drying. Some surface-active anionic agents are recommended to act as reserving agents for the nylon in large-scale work, particularly with pale shades.

The following experiment illustrates the differential uptake of a levelling acid dye by wool and nylon, and the effect of an anionic auxiliary on the distribution of the dye between the two fibres.

Procedure

To simulate an 80/20 blend of wool/nylon, prepare seven composite samples consisting each of a 1 g piece of nylon fabric and a 4 g piece of wool fabric. These are dyed in the dyebaths given in Table 6.1. Enter the composite specimens at about 40°C, raise the temperature to the boil and dye for 30 min. Rinse in warm water and dry.

TABLE 6.1

	Amount (% o.w.f.)						
	I	II	III	IV	V	VI	VII
C.I. Acid Red 1	0.1	0.1	0.1	0.1	0.1	1	3
Anionic surface-active agent (g/l)	0.1	0.2	0.5	1.0			
Glauber's salt	10	10	10	10	10	10	10
Formic acid	4	4	4	4	4	4	4

Liquor ratio 60:1

Results

1. By comparison of composite dyeings V, VI and VII, explain the observed differences in uptake by the two fibres in terms of their chemical structures.
2. By comparison of dyeings I, II, III, IV and V, comment on the effect of the anionic surface-active agent on the distribution of dye between the two fibres. Would you expect this effect to be influenced at all by the degree of sulphonation of the dye?
3. Using the *Colour Index*, select which of the following dyes would be most suitable in admixture with C.I. Acid Red 1 for producing uniform shades on wool/nylon blends:
   - C.I. Acid Yellow 17
   - C.I. Acid Yellow 29
   - C.I. Acid Yellow 65
   - C.I. Acid Blue 23
   - C.I. Acid Blue 40
   - C.I. Acid Blue 47
   - C.I. Acid Blue 80.

6.2 THE DYEING OF A WOOL/POLYESTER MIXTURE

By blending polyester with wool, fabrics are obtained with improved wear and crease resistance in addition to the desirable warmth and handle of pure wool, and these are widely used in men's suiting. Optimum colour fastness of this blend results from the polyester and wool being dyed separately prior to blending. However, in many cases it is necessary for the material to be dyed in blend form. The choice of suitable dyes for the blend is confined to disperse for the polyester and neutral-dyeing acid or 1:2 metal-complex types for the wool, but a number of factors may restrict this choice further. Thus normally only class B or C disperse dyes are used, and certain azo disperse dyes are sensitive to the mild reducing action of cysteine in damaged wool. At lower temperatures the wool component is preferentially dyed by the disperse dyes, particularly the lower molecular weight azo types, though at the boil and in the presence of a carrier the rate of dyeing on the polyester is greatly increased. The choice of carrier is also important and factors such as odour, tendency to staining of the wool, yellowing effects on exposure to light, and cost must be considered.

The following experiment illustrates the advantages of dyeing this type of mixture by a two-bath method (where the two components are dyed separately) over the shorter one-bath method. In the former the wool is 'cleared' of disperse dye by an alkaline reducing treatment before dyeing with the acid dye. Although a lengthier process, the two-bath method gives optimum wet fastness properties.

Procedure

1. Equal weights of wool and polyester are taken and combined to simulate a 50/50 blend, then dyed using disperse dyes for the polyester and milling acid types for the wool, to give a solid shade. Use 2 g pieces of wool and polyester and prepare dyebaths as shown in Table 6.2, basing the amounts of dye on the amounts of each of the fibre types present. In the one-bath method enter the wetted out composite patterns at 40°C. Raise to the boil and maintain for 1 h. Finally rinse and dry. In the two-bath method dye the polyester first as follows. Enter the wetted out composite patterns at 40°C. Raise to the boil and maintain for 1 h. Remove small pieces of the wool and polyester at this stage.

TABLE 6.2

	Amount (% o.w.f.)		
		Two-bath method	
	One-bath method	Polyester	Wool
C.I. Disperse Violet 33	10	10	
C.I. Acid Red 129	0.5		0.5
Carrier (Matexil CA-MN (ICI)) (g/l)	6	6	
Glauber's salt (g/l)	8		8

Liquor ratio 50:1

Rinse cold, then carry out reduction clearing for 15 min at 50°C in a solution containing:
– Ammonia (sp. gr. 0.880), 4 ml/l
– Sodium dithionite, 3 g/l
– Matexil (DN-VL) (ICI), 0.5 ml/l
– Liquor ratio 50:1.

Rinse for a further 15 min in cold water containing 1 g/l glacial acetic acid. Remove further small samples of wool and polyester. To dye the wool component, add the patterns to a fresh dyebath at 40°C containing the recipe given in Table 6.2. Raise to the boil and maintain at this temperature for 45 min. Rinse and dry.
2. Carry out an ISO 3 wash fastness test on a 'blend' sample from each of the above dyeings.
3. There are certain ranges of dyes available for domestic dyeing. The Dylon Multi-purpose range consists of mixtures of dyes designed to cope with a variety of fibres. Using 10% of Dylon dye 44 in this range and 2 g pieces of wool and polyester to simulate a 50/50 blend, carry out a dyeing at a liquor ratio of 50:1. Enter the composite specimen at 40°C, raise the temperature to 85°C and dye for 2 h. Rinse and dry.

Results
1. Compare the shades obtained on both fibres of the 'blend' using the one-bath and two-bath methods.
2. From the samples removed, note the effect of the reduction clearing treatment on the wool. Why is there no apparent effect with the polyester?
3. Compare the wash fastness of the composite dyeings from the one-bath and two-bath methods, and comment on the results.
4. Comment on the result from the Dylon dyeing and on the difficulties involved in preparing suitable mixtures of dye classes for multi-purpose domestic dyeing.

6.3 THE DYEING OF POLYESTER/COTTON BLENDS BY DIFFERENT METHODS

Blends of polyester and cotton (ranging from 50/50 to 70/30) are of major importance to the textile industry. They are relatively cheap to produce and possess a number of qualities which make them ideal for a wide range of uses including shirts, blouses, overalls, raincoats and other lightweight garments. The physical properties of the components impart to such fabrics the feel and moisture absorbency of cotton, and the resistance to wear and dimensional stability associated with polyester.

Careful preparation of polyester/cotton fabric prior to dyeing is necessary for successful results later, but otherwise there are comparatively few technical limitations in the dyeing of blends of this type. Disperse dyes are used almost exclusively for the polyester component and although these will generally stain cotton, a reduction clear treatment will reduce this. The cotton component itself can be dyed with most classes of dye available for that fibre; it is possible to use direct dyes by a one-bath technique, though the wet fastness obtained in this way will usually only satisfy the lowest requirements. For batch dyeing the method of dyeing is limited by available equipment, time, economics and the fastness requirements for the end product. A number of continuous dyeing methods may also be used to colour fabrics of this type, making use of:
(a) Solubilised vat dyes for pale shades of high fastness
(b) Disperse/reactive dyes for pale and medium shades of good fastness
(c) Disperse/vat mixtures for optimum fastness.

The main disadvantage of such padding techniques is the requirement for suitable equipment.

The following experiment illustrates a number of batch dyeing methods which can be used for this particular blend, and compares the wash fastnesses of the resulting dyeings.

Procedure

(a) Disperse/direct – two-bath method

Prepare the two dyebaths as indicated in Table 6.3, using a 5 g piece of polyester/cotton fabric (all percentages are based on the total weight of fabric). Enter the wetted out fabric into dyebath I at 50°C, quickly raise the temperature to 120°C and dye for 30 min. Remove, rinse and carry out a reduction clearing treatment with a solution containing 5 g/l sodium hydroxide and 2 g/l sodium dithionite for 15 min at 60°C at a liquor ratio of 50:1. Remove, rinse well in cold water and transfer the sample to dyebath II pre-set at 50°C. Raise the temperature to about 95°C and dye for 30 min. Rinse and enter the fabric into a third bath containing 2% of a proprietory aftertreating agent, e.g. Matexil FC-PN (ICI). Treat for 20 min at 40°C at a liquor ratio of 50:1. Wash thoroughly in a 2 g/l soap solution for 20 min at 50°C. Rinse and dry.

TABLE 6.3

	Amount (% o.w.f.)	
	I	II
C.I. Disperse Violet 33	4	
Acetic acid (glacial)	1.5	
C.I. Direct Red 83		2
Sodium chloride		20

Liquor ratio 30:1

(b) Disperse/direct – one-bath, high-temperature method

Prepare the dyebath as follows for a 5 g piece of polyester/cotton fabric:
– C.I. Disperse Violet 33, 4%
– C.I. Direct Red 83, 2%
– Sodium chloride, 20%
– Acetic acid (glacial), 1.5%.

Enter the wetted out fabric at 50°C and raise the temperature to 120°C. Dye for 30 min at a liquor ratio of 30:1. Remove and aftertreat in a 2% solution of a proprietory after-treating agent (see (a) above), following this with a treatment in 2 g/l soap solution for 20 min at 50°C. Rinse and dry.

(c) Disperse/direct – one-bath with carrier method

Repeat procedure (b) but with the addition of 0.3% Matexil CA-MN (ICI) and dye at 100°C for 1 h.

(d) Disperse/reactive method
Prepare the dyebaths shown in Table 6.4 for a 5 g piece of polyester/cotton fabric. Enter the wetted out fabric into dyebath I at 60°C, raise to 120°C and dye for 30 min. Carry out a reduction clear treatment with a solution containing 5 g/l sodium hydroxide and 2 g/l sodium dithionite for 15 min at 60°C. Rinse well in cold water. Prepare dyebath II without the sodium chloride or alkalis, add the fabric at 60°C and dye for 10 min. Add the sodium chloride, agitate for 5–10 min and complete the dyebath by addition of the alkalis. Dye for a further 30 min. Remove and treat the sample in a solution of 2 g/l soap solution for 20 min at 90°C.

TABLE 6.4

	Amount (% o.w.f.)	
	I	II
C.I. Disperse Violet 33	4	
Acetic acid (glacial)	1.5	
C.I. Reactive Red 6		4
Sodium chloride		30
Sodium carbonate		1.5
Sodium bicarbonate		1.5

Liquor ratio 50:1

(e) Disperse/vat method
Prepare the dyebaths shown in Table 6.5 for a 5 g piece of polyester/cotton fabric. Enter the wetted out fabric in dyebath I at 60°C, raise to 120°C and dye for 30 min. Rinse and transfer to dyebath II prepared by the usual vatting procedure (see section 4.6). Dye for 40 min at 50°C. Rinse well with cold water then allow to oxidise in hydrogen peroxide solution. Finally treat with a solution of 5 g/l soap and 2 g/l sodium carbonate at the boil for 30 min. Rinse and dry.

Carry out wash fastness tests at 95°C on portions of each of the five dyeings. If time permits, carry out rub fastness tests on dyeings (a), (b) and (c).

Results
1. Visually examine each sample, and comment on any variation in levelness. In the case of dyeings (a), (b) and (c) note any variation in depth between the three dyeings.
2. Using the grey scales, assess the wash fastnesses of all the dyeings.
3. With reference to the time and complexity of dyeing procedures, coupled with the quality and fastness of the dyed products, discuss, from a commercial dyer's point of view, the merits of each method of dyeing with respect to profitability in the production of, for example, shirts and blouses. Note that the general increasing order of dye prices is direct < disperse < reactive < vat.

TABLE 6.5

	Amount (% o.w.f.)	
	I	II
C.I. Disperse Violet 33	4	
Acetic acid (glacial)	1.5	
C.I. Vat Red 21		5
Sodium dithionite		4
Sodium hydroxide		8
Non-ionic dispersing agent (g/l)		1

Liquor ratio 50:1

4. Why is a separate reduction clear treatment not necessary in method (e) and undesirable in method (b)?
5. Comment on the problems associated with the colour matching of the two components in the blend.
6. Assess the rub fastness of dyeings (a), (b) and (c), and comment on the results.

REFERENCES

1. J Shore in 'The dyeing of synthetic-polymer and acetate fibres', Ed. D M Nunn (Bradford: Dyers' Company Publications Trust, 1979).
2. W J Marshall in 'The dyeing of cellulosic fibres', Ed. C Preston (Bradford: Dyers' Company Publications Trust, 1985).

7 NATURAL DYES

Until the advent of synthetic dyes in the second half of the nineteenth century all colouring matters were derived directly from vegetable or animal sources. Of these only logwood is used today as a textile dye and then only for specialised purposes such as black shades on silk and leather. Although material for jeans is often dyed with indigo, it is the synthetic and not the naturally occurring form of the dyestuff that is employed for this purpose. With the increasing interest in health foods, a number of naturally occurring colorants find use in the food industry. A number of yellow polyenes, e.g. carotenes, saffron and annatto, are the main natural colorants in butter, margarine and cheese. The water-soluble saffron is ideally suited as a replacement for the well known synthetic dye tartrazine (C.I. Food Yellow 4) in many foods, and turmeric gives curry dishes their characteristic yellow colour. Though once an important dye, the red anthraquinone derivative cochineal is now only used in confectionery.

While in former times local small-scale dyers must have obtained their colorants from sources such as flowers, berries, lichens, etc., the production of dyed material on an industrial scale relied heavily on a few established natural dyes. The madder plant afforded the most important red dye (alizarin), though three reds from insect sources, kermes, cochineal and lac, were also widely used. These all require mordants and most highly prized was the famous Turkey red produced from madder using a mordant of calcium and aluminium salts. Yellows were obtainable from the flavonoid group of colorants, which include weld, quercitin and Persian berries, and these were also applied using a mordanting technique. The yellow shades obtained on wool with, for example, quercitin using a tin mordant were as brilliant as those now available from the brightest reactive dyes. Blue was produced almost exclusively from indigo, while the formation of green shades normally involved the overdyeing of a yellow with indigo. Beautiful though very fugitive purple and mauve shades were obtained from certain lichens in the presence of a nitrogen donor (ammonia or stale urine). The dye was marketed as orchil, archil or cudbear.

Logwood was by far the most important black dye from the 16th century onwards. The colouring matter haematein is itself red, but when applied in the presence of a chromium salt it gives a black shade on a number of fibres, e.g. wool, silk and nylon, unsurpassed by most synthetic dyes.

Many of the natural dyes consisted of a number of coloured components and the final shade obtained was to some extent dependent on the proportion of these components, a factor which in turn varied according to source, season, and dyeing conditions. Despite these difficulties, and also the dyeing methods used, which sometimes lasted for weeks at a time, some beautiful examples of early dyed fabrics remain in museums and collections, a testament to the skill and expertise of the dyers in those times. The experiments described below are designed to illustrate the application properties of some of the more readily obtainable of the early natural dyes.

7.1 INDIGO ON WOOL AND COTTON

Indigo, a naturally occurring blue vat dye, has for several thousand years been extensively used in the dyeing of wool and cotton, and there is evidence of its use in the colouring of ancient Egyptian mummy cloths. Until the end of the 19th century indigo was exclusively obtained from a variety of plants indigenous mainly to tropical regions of the world. The elucidation of the chemical constitution of the main colouring matter, indigotin, and the subsequent discovery of a method to produce indigotin synthetically, brought the production of natural indigo to an almost complete halt.

Indigo can be used to dye cotton and wool to give dyeings of excellent wash and light fastness. Sulphonation of indigo gives as the main product the 5,5'-disulphonate, a commercial acid dye, and although this treatment confers water solubility upon the parent insoluble vat dye and gives a brighter hue than the parent compound, subsequent dyeings have poor fastness properties, particularly with respect to light.

Synthetic indigo is still extensively used although it is now almost exclusively confined to the dyeing of cotton denim garments. Its popularity has endured, and the following experiment illustrates the dyeing and fastness properties of one of the most famous of all colouring matters on wool and on cotton.

Procedure

1. (a) Prepare the dyebath given below for a 5 g piece of wool fabric, dyeing at a liquor ratio of 40:1:
   – C.I. Vat Blue 1 (indigo), 3%
   – Sodium dithionite, 2%
   – Gelatin solution (1%), 40 ml/l
   – Ammonia (sp. gr. 0.880), 10 ml/l.

   Heat the water alone to about 55°C, add the ammonia and about half the sodium dithionite. Allow to stand for about 5 min. Add the gelatin solution and the dye. Stir well and add the remainder of the sodium dithionite. Allow to stand for 15 min. If the solution is incompletely reduced, add slightly more sodium dithionite. Complete reduction is indicated by the dyebath maintaining a clear greenish-yellow colour. At 50°C enter the wetted out pattern and dye for 30 min at this temperature. Remove, squeeze and allow to oxidise in air. After complete oxidation, rinse well. Soap at the boil for about 15 min, rinse and dry.

   (b) Prepare a dyebath as above using 1.5% dye for a 5 g piece of wool fabric. Carry out an identical dyeing procedure up to and including oxidation. After complete oxidation, instead of soaping, re-enter the pattern to the still reduced dyebath for 10 min at 50°C. Remove and oxidise in air. Following oxidation, re-enter the dyed pattern for 10 min at 50°C. Repeat this procedure until the depth of shade matches that of the result of part (a). Soap and rinse as before.

2. (a) Prepare the dyebath given below for a 5 g piece of bleached cotton fabric, dyeing at a liquor ratio of 40:1:
   – C.I. Vat Blue 1, 3%
   – Sodium hydroxide (solid), 10%
   – Sodium dithionite, 7%.

   Heat the water to about 70°C. Carry out the normal vatting procedure (see section 4.6). Allow to stand for about 15 min, adding more sodium dithionite if necessary to effect complete reduction. Enter the wetted out sample and dye for 30 min at 70°C. Remove, squeeze and oxidise in air. After completion of the oxidation stage (about 10 min) rinse and soap at the boil for 15 min. Rinse and dry.

(b) Prepare a dyebath, as above, using 1.5% of the same dye, for a similar 5 g piece of cotton fabric. Carry out the procedure as detailed in 1(b) for the dyeing of wool with indigo, but at 70°C. Give the sample four dips in total.

3. The following fastness comparisons can be made:

(a) Fastness to washing of indigo on cotton (ISO 4) and wool (ISO 3)

(b) Light fastness of indigo and sulphonated indigo (C.I. Acid Blue 74, C.I. Food Blue 1) on wool. C.I. Acid Blue 74 is applied as a levelling acid dye (see section 3.2).

Results

1. Compare the results of the cotton dyeings with those of the wool, especially the effect of successive dips, on depth of shade.
2. Assess the number of dips of the 1.5% dyeing required to match the 3% dyeing on wool.
3. Explain why ammonia is used in the wool dyebath rather than sodium hydroxide.
4. Assess the wash fastness of indigo on wool and cotton and the light fastness of indigo and sulphonated indigo on wool.
5. 6,6'-Dibromoindigo is the famous Tyrian purple, and is a rare example of a naturally occurring bromo-compound. Students of organic chemistry should write the structure of Tyrian purple and explain whether or not it would be the likely product of the laboratory bromination of indigo.

7.2 ALIZARIN ON WOOL – THE EFFECT OF MORDANTS

Alizarin (1,2-dihydroxyanthraquinone) is one of a number of naturally occurring anthraquinones found in the root of the madder plant, *Rubia tinctorum*. It is not itself a dye but forms insoluble coloured lakes with a number of metals that can be deposited in wool and cotton fibres, and the art of dyeing with madder was practised by the early Indians, Persians and Egyptians. The most famous of the colours produced is Turkey red, a complex of alizarin with aluminium and calcium that gives a red of great brilliance and permanence on cotton fabric, though the dyeing process is an extremely lengthy one.

Alizarin, described at one time as the most important of all dyes, was isolated in 1824 from the action of strong sulphuric acid on madder.

Alizarin may be used to produce a range of hues and the effect of different mordants on the eventual colour is illustrated in the following experiment.

Procedure

1. Prepare four mordanting baths as shown in Table 7.1 for 2 g pieces of wool fabric. Make up each bath to 100–150 ml with deionised water, enter the pieces of wool and bring to the boil. Boil, with stirring, for 30 min. Rinse well in cold water.
2. Prepare the alizarin baths by weighing out 0.5 g alizarin and heating it at the boil in 150 ml deionised water. Decant off the clear solution. Boil the residue with more deionised water and continue decanting until a clear solution of alizarin is obtained. Separate the combined decanted solutions into four equal portions, adjusting the pH of each to 6–7 and the liquor ratio to 50:1. Enter the mordanted wool pieces and bring to the boil. Dye for 45 min at the boil. Remove from the dyebath and rinse well in water. Repeat the mordanting and dyeing procedures for dyeing II (aluminium mordant), omitting the cold water rinse at the end of the mordanting stage. Check the pH of the dyebath before dyeing.

TABLE 7.1

	Amount (% o.w.f.)			
	I	II	III	IV
Potassium dichromate	10			
Aluminium sulphate		10		
Tin(II) chloride			10	
Iron(II) sulphate				10
Potassium hydrogen tartrate	3	7		3
Sulphuric acid (dilute)		to pH 3		

3. If time permits, carry out ISO 3 wash fastness tests on dyeings I–IV.

Results
1. Comment on the range of hues obtained with alizarin and different mordants.
2. Compare the dyeings obtained with the aluminium mordant under 2. (both with and without the cold water rinse), and comment on the effect of pH on the formation of the alizarin–metal complex.
3. If possible compare the wash fastness properties at 60°C of the alizarin dyeings with those of similar depth and shade using levelling or milling acid dyes.
4. Students of dye chemistry should identify two possible sites in the alizarin molecule where complex formation with the metal could take place, and by examination of the dyeings suggest which is the likelier in practice.

7.3 LOGWOOD ON WOOL
Logwood was at one time a very important dyestuff. It is the product of a large leguminous tree *Haematoxylon campechianum* which grows in the West Indies and South America. The colouring matter of logwood, haematin, is dark red, but in the presence of mordants it gives blue, violet or black hues on wool, these being the colours obtained from copper, tin and chromium salts respectively. Its use is now restricted to the specialised dyeing of silk and leather. Addition of fustic to the dyebath is said to increase the fastness to light, and a third bath is often used to fix the colouring matter. This experiment illustrates these effects.

Procedure
Carry out the following on two 2 g pieces of wool fabric.
1. Prepare a mordanting bath containing 3% potassium dichromate and 4% potassium hydrogen tartrate, using a liquor ratio of 50:1 Enter the wetted out wool at 80°C, raise to the boil and maintain for 30 min. Rinse thoroughly with water.
2. Prepare the dyebaths shown in Table 7.2. Enter the wet mordanted pieces of fabric at 80°C, one into each dyebath. Raise to the boil and maintain at this temperature for 30 min.
3. Take half of dyeing I and add it to a fixing solution containing 1% potassium dichromate at a liquor ratio of 50:1 at 75°C. Treat the dyed fabric for 15 min in this bath, ensuring

TABLE 7.2

| | Amount (% o.w.f.) | |
	I	II
Logwood chips	15	15
Fustic		5

Liquor ratio 50:1

that the temperature does not rise above 80°C. Rinse thoroughly with water and dry.
4. Carry out light fastness tests on dyeings I and II.
5. Carry out wash fastness tests (ISO 3) on the unfixed and fixed portions of dyeing I.

Results
1. Assess the light fastness of dyeings I and II using the blue wool standards and comment on any effect of the added fustic.
2. Assess the wash fastness of the unfixed and fixed portions of dyeing I using the grey scales, and indicate whether the fixing aftertreatment improves the wash fastness of logwood. Why should such a treatment be expected to improve the overall wet fastness properties of logwood blacks?

7.4 COCHINEAL ON WOOL
Cochineal is one of the few natural dyes obtained from the animal kingdom, being derived from a species of insect indigenous to Mexico. Approximately 200 000 insects are required for 1 kg of dyestuff. Cochineal dominated the European market in red shades for over 400 years, and at its peak in the late 19th century more than 500 tonnes were imported annually into Europe. Present textile usage is practically nil as it has been been superseded by cheaper modern synthetic dyes. For many years cochineal was used in the colouring of the scarlet ceremonial uniforms of certain sections of the British army and it is still used as a food colorant today, as well as in the manufacture of red and pink lakes and inks. Like alizarin, cochineal is an anthraquinone derivative and the colouring matter constituent, a salt of carminic acid, occurs to the extent of about 10% of the dried crushed insects.

In the dyeing of wool with cochineal the colouring matter is applied to previously mordanted wool, the colours obtained being dependent on the mordant used. Thus tin, chromium, aluminium and copper give scarlet, purple, crimson and claret colours respectively, though in practice only tin and aluminium have been used to any great extent. Mordanting with these metal salts gives two shades of red, cochineal scarlet and cochineal crimson respectively, and the following experiment illustrates this, as well as the pH sensitivity of the dye.

Procedure
1. Carry out the two-bath procedure outlined in Table 7.3 on two 5 g pieces of wool fabric. Enter the wetted out wool at 60°C into the mordanting bath (bath 1). Raise to the boil

TABLE 7.3

| | Amount (% o.w.f.) | | |
| | Bath 1 | | |
	I	II	Bath 2
Tin(II) chloride	5		
Aluminium sulphate		5	
Potassium hydrogen tartrate	5	5	
Ground cochineal			20

Liquor ratio 40:1

and gently boil for 30 min, maintaining the volume. Rinse in cold water. Then enter the wetted out wool into the dyebath (bath 2) at 60°C, slowly raise to the boil and boil gently for 30 min, maintaining the volume. Rinse and dry.
2. Prepare four buffer solutions covering the pH range 3–10, e.g. approx. 3, 5, 8 and 10. Place small pieces from each of the dyeings into the four solutions and leave for 15 min. Remove and dry.

Results
1. Comment on the effect of the two mordants on the colours obtained with cochineal.
2. (a) Comment on the effect of pH on these colours.
   (b) Students of dye chemistry should look up the structure of cochineal (C.I. 75470) and indicate which structural features might be responsible for any colour change.
3. The wash fastness (ISO 2) of tin-mordanted cochineal on wool has been given as:
   – Effect on pattern   1
   – Staining of wool   4–5.

Explain these figures.

8 ADVANCED EXPERIMENTS ON DYE UPTAKE AND COLOUR MEASUREMENT

In this chapter we turn to a series of more advanced experiments for which expensive equipment may be required (e.g. recording spectrophotometers) and for which the background theory is given in Part III. It is recommended that the student should read and try to understand the background theory appropriate to the experiment (as indicated at the start of each), preferably before attempting the practical work, but certainly before analysing the results and writing the report.

The experiments in this section utilise spectrophotometry and colorimetry both for following dye uptake and for recording the colour of the dyed samples produced. These techniques may of course have been used in some of the earlier experiments as indicated in section 2.3. Note that in order to avoid extensive description of the equipment, it is recommended that students should have available appropriate instrument instruction manuals and other background information and references as indicated.

8.1 LIGHT ABSORPTION BY DYE SOLUTIONS (BEER'S LAW)
(see sections 11.1–11.3)

A dilute solution of a dye has a characteristic absorption spectrum in the visible region (400–700 nm) of the electromagnetic spectrum and the position and shape of this determines the colour of the solution. The intensity of absorption changes with the concentration of the dye (c) and the path length of the solution (l) through which the light passes. This dependence is implicit in the Beer–Lambert law of light absorption (Eqn 8.1):

$$A = kcl \qquad (8.1)$$

where A = absorbance (as defined in section 11.1)

$\quad\ c$ = concentration in solution of the absorbing substance (dye in solution)

$\quad\ l$ = path length of the analysing light beam through the absorbing solution (cell length)

$\quad\ k$ = proportionality constant known as the absorption coefficient (or absorptivity), whose value depends on the units used for c and l.

When c is in units of mol/l and l is in cm, the proportionality constant is usually known as the molar absorption coefficient (ε), with units of l/(mol cm).

For this experiment two different types of visible region instruments (absorptiometers or spectrophotometers) should be available or one instrument should be operated at two significantly different slit widths. It is assumed that the student will be instructed on the normal operating procedure, which allows absorbance values to be recorded at suitable wavelength intervals over the visible region. Beer's law is said to hold if the plot of A versus c at fixed values of l is linear over the range measured (approx. $A = 0$ to $A = 2$).

Procedure

Using a levelling acid dye of good solubility (e.g. C.I. Acid Red 1) prepare a stock solution in deionised water at a concentration of 0.1 g/l.

1. Prepare by dilution in, say, 50 ml flasks, a series of concentrations: 0.01, 0.02, 0.03, 0.04 and 0.05 g/l, diluting with deionised water accurately.
2. Prepare also two further solutions at 0.05 g/l, diluting with 20% ammonia solution and 20% acetic acid solution respectively.
3. Record the absorption curves in 10 mm cells (cuvettes) as absorbance versus wavelength over the visible region (400–700 nm) (at 20 nm intervals if a manual instrument is being used) for the three 0.05 g/l solutions (aqueous, ammoniacal and acidic), using a blank 10 mm cell containing water only as reference.
4. If the instrument has facilities for recording $\log A$ values, or if time permits doing it by hand, record the $\log A$ curve for the aqueous solution at 0.05 and 0.02 g/l over the wavelength region 400–700 nm.
5. Note the wavelength of maximum absorption (λ_{max}) for the aqueous solution of dye and measure the absorbance values of the five dilutions (0.01–0.05 g/l) on both instruments (or on the single instrument at normal and, say, five times normal slit widths) using cells of the same path length.

Results

1. Comment on whether acetic acid or ammonia affects the shape of the absorption curve, and hence the colour of the dye solution.
2. Show that the shape of the $\log A$ versus wavelength curve (but not A vs wavelength) is independent of concentration.
3. Plot values of A_{max} versus concentration for the two instrumental conditions.
4. Comment on the applicability, or otherwise, of Beer's law under the two instrumental conditions.
5. Calculate appropriate values of the absorptivity k (absorption coefficient), note carefully the units used, and compare with literature values [1] .

8.2 LIGHT REFLECTANCE FROM DYED FABRICS (KUBELKA–MUNK ANALYSIS)

(see sections 11.4–11.6)

The colour of a piece of dyed fabric depends on the manner in which visible light (400–700 nm) is differentially reflected from it. Increasing the concentration or strength of the dye on the fabric results in a decrease in the reflectance (R) of the dyeing, which is most marked at the wavelength corresponding closely to the wavelength of maximum absorption (λ_{max}) of the dye in solution.

In this experiment choose three wool dyes of different colour (say, red, yellow and blue) and initially compare the solution absorption curves with the reflectance curves for the same dyes on wool fabric at suitable concentrations. For one of the dyes the variation of the reflectance curve with dye concentration on the fabric is recorded, and the reflectance at λ_{max} fitted to the Kubelka–Munk expression (Eqn 8.2), where R is the reflectance factor of the sample ($R = R\%/100$):

$$\mathrm{f}(R) = \frac{(1 - R)^2}{2R} \tag{8.2}$$

The linearity of the plot of $f(R)$ versus dye concentration (c) is tested. The slope of this graph gives the absorption coefficient (α) used as calibration data in computer colour matching experiments (section 8.10).

Procedure
The following are required for this experiment:
(a)   Aqueous solutions of a red, yellow and blue dye for wool (e.g. level-dyeing acid dyes[1]) at about 0.01 g/l (i.e. to give absorbance values at λ_{max} in the range 0.5 to 1.5).
(b)   Samples of wool dyed with the above dyes at concentrations in the range 0% (undyed) to 1.0% o.w.f.
(c)   A recording spectrophotometer capable of measuring both solution and reflectance spectra over the visible region (400–700 nm) (a reflectance attachment is normally used).

1.   Record the absorbance spectrum of each of the three dye solutions in 10 mm cells over the visible spectrum (or at 20 nm intervals). For each dye solution note the wavelength range over which the absorbance is a least half that at λ_{max}.
2.   Choose the 0.5% dyeing for each of the three dyes and record the reflectance spectra over the visible spectrum using a suitable reference white (tile or pressed barium sulphate). For each dyeing, note the wavelength range over which the reflectance drops to at least half the maximum drop at λ_{max}.
3.   For one dyed fabric concentration series (e.g. the reds) record on the same chart the reflectance spectra over the visible region. Include a blank or undyed sample.
4.   From the results, tabulate the variation of percentage reflectance (R) at λ_{max} (reflectance minimum) with concentration (c). Prepare plots of R versus c and of $f(R)$ versus c .

Results
1.   Comment on the relationship between the absorbance and reflectance curve characteristics [2].
2.   Explain why the blank has $f(R)_w > 0$ at most wavelengths
3.   Note the non-linearity of the R vs c plot, and comment on the degree of linearity of the Kubelka–Munk plot.
4.   Evaluate the slope of the $f(R)$ vs c plot, note the units and fit to the equation (Eqn 8.3):

$$f(R) = f(R)_w + \alpha c \tag{8.3}$$

If appropriate, compare the absorption coefficient (α) with the calibration data held in the computer data file of the experiment in section 8.10.

8.3   LIGHT ABSORPTION/REFLECTANCE OF DYE MIXTURES
(see section 11.7)
The use of spectrophotometry in the analysis of dye mixtures, either in solution or on a dyed substrate, depends on the additivity of the absorbances (A) for the components of the mixture in solution or of the linear reflectance function $f(R)$ for dyed substrates. In this

---

1. Calibration dyeings. Note that if the computer colour matching experiment (section 8.10) is to be done, the dyes chosen for this experiment could be taken as those selected in section 8.10 and Appendix B. This would allow the student to check the calibration data used on the computer.

experiment we examine the analysis for two- and three-dye mixtures on a substrate using reflectance measurements, and the following experiment (section 8.4) analyses a mixture of two dyes in solution.

The relationship between the reflectance (R) and the concentration of dye (c) for a thick opaque pattern is given by the Kubelka–Munk equation (Eqn 8.4) (see section 8.2):

$$K/S = \frac{(1 - R)^2}{2R} = f(R) \tag{8.4}$$

R is in the form of a decimal fraction; for example, for a reflectance of 50%, $R = 0.5$, so $K/S = 0.25$. S is the coefficient of scatter and is constant for a thick opaque material. K is the coefficient of absorption and is proportional to the concentration of dye c, with a contribution from the undyed white material (substrate) w (Eqn 8.5):

$$K = \alpha c + K_w \tag{8.5}$$

For a particular dye the constant α (the calibration factor or absorption coefficient) is readily obtained from the reflectance of dyeings of known concentration (c). It is necessary, however, to correct for absorption of light by the undyed material or white material. Hence Eqn 8.6 can be written:

$$f(R) = f(R_p) - f(R_w) = \alpha c \tag{8.6}$$

where p = pattern and w = white.

For example, a pattern dyed with 0.5% C. I. Acid Blue 41 has a reflectance of 9.4% at 620 nm whilst the undyed material has a reflectance of 72%. Insertion of the corresponding calculated K/S values in Eqn 8.6 gives f(R) = 4.37 – 0.06 = 4.31, which then gives $\alpha = 8.62$. (For dyes in solution the corresponding function is the absorbance A related to concentration at fixed path length by $A = kc$ (see experiments in sections 8.1. and 8.4).

For two-component mixtures, say, of dyes x and y at concentrations c_x and c_y we require measurements at two wavelengths to give Eqns 8.7 and 8.8:

$$\text{At } \lambda_1 \quad f(R_1) = \alpha_{1,x} c_x + \alpha_{1,y} c_y \tag{8.7}$$

$$\text{At } \lambda_2 \quad f(R_2) = \alpha_{2,x} c_x + \alpha_{2,y} c_y \tag{8.8}$$

These are two simultaneous equations which can readily be solved for c_x and c_y.

If three dyes (x, y and z) are present, absorption is again assumed additive and for the three-dye mixture Eqn 8.9 applies:

$$K = \alpha_x c_x + \alpha_y c_y + \alpha_z c_z + K_w \tag{8.9}$$

Alternatively we can write Eqn 8.10:

$$f(R) = A c_x + B c_y + C c_z \tag{8.10}$$

where A, B and C are the calibration factors (α) obtained from dyeings of dyes x, y and z of known concentration.

The reflectance of the dyed pattern, containing unknown amounts of three dyes (e.g. a yellow, a red and a blue) is measured at three appropriate wavelengths (λ_1, λ_2, λ_3), e.g. at 420, 520 and 620 nm, giving R_1, R_2 and R_3. Then, after correcting for the reflectance of the substrate at the three wavelengths, Eqn 8.11 can be written:

$$\text{At } \lambda_1 \quad f(R_1) = A_1 c_x + B_1 c_y + C_1 c_z$$

$$\text{At } \lambda_2 \quad f(R_2) = A_2 c_x + B_2 c_y + C_2 c_z$$

$$\text{At } \lambda_3 \quad f(R_3) = A_3 c_x + B_3 c_y + C_3 c_z \qquad (8.11)$$

These three equations can be solved to obtain the required three quantities c_x, c_y and c_z, but the solution is best found by matrix algebra as discussed in the theory section 11.7. However, in the present experiment some of the calibration factors are zero and the solution is simplified as detailed below.

Procedure[1]

A wool pattern, e.g. a light grey, dyed with the dyes shown in Table 8.1 is provided as an unknown (the dyes chosen might be the same as those used in experiments in sections 8.2 and 8.10).

The nine calibration coefficients A_1, A_2 ... C_2, C_3 need to be available from standard single-dye dyeings at the three wavelengths in Table 8.1.

TABLE 8.1

	Dye	λ_{max} (nm)
x	C.I. Acid Yellow 29	420
y	C.I. Acid Red 57	520
z	C.I. Acid Blue 41	620

1. If necessary, prepare standard dyeings using conditions for acid levelling dyes (section 3.2) and obtain the calibration coefficients.
2. Measure the reflectance of the unknown pattern and the undyed substrate (wool) at the three wavelengths shown in Table 8.1.
3. Substitute the values of R_1, R_2 and R_3 into the equations as shown in the calculations, and solve for c_x, c_y and c_z.
4. Prepare a dyeing with these calculated concentrations and compare with the original pattern supplied (the reflectance curves could be compared and the computed values of X, Y, Z, L^*, a^*, b^* listed, along with the colour difference ΔE under illuminant D_{65} (see experiments in sections 8.9 and 8.10).

1. Note: To simplify the experiment the unknown could be a purple dyeing prepared by dyeing a red and blue mixture only. Measurements and calibration data are then only required at 520 and 620 nm, and the simultaneous equations can be solved by hand calculation.

Results
1. Mount small samples of the unknown and the dyed matching pattern side by side.
2. Comment on the closeness of the match, and the possible sources of error.
3. Show the calculations as below.

Calculations
The steps in the solution of Eqn 8.11 are illustrated below using data obtained from 0.5% dyeings, and taking typical reflectance values for a light grey pattern which is to be matched. The student should substitute the values obtained from his or her own dyeings and unknown pattern, which have been prepared and measured as described above.

(a) *From 0.5% dyeings* (Table 8.2)

TABLE 8.2

	Undyed wool (w)	C.I. Acid Yellow 29	C.I. Acid Red 57	C.I. Acid Blue 41
Dye concentration (c): = 0.5%				
$\lambda_1 = 420$ nm, R	48%	5.0%	26%	35%
$f(R)$	0.28	9.02	1.05	0.604
$f(R_p) - f(R_w)$		8.74	0.77	0.324
$[f(R_p) - f(R_w)]/c$		$A_1 = 17.5$	$B_1 = 1.54$	$C_1 = 0.648$
$\lambda_2 = 520$ nm, R	69%	69%	6.5%	17%
$f(R)$	0.07	0.07	6.73	2.03
$f(R_p) - f(R_w)$		0	6.66	1.96
$[f(R_p) - f(R_w)]/c$		$A_2 = 0$	$B_2 = 13.3$	$C_2 = 3.92$
$\lambda_3 = 620$ nm, R	79%	79%	79%	6.0%
$f(R)$	0.03	0.03	0.03	7.36
$f(R_p) - f(R_w)$		0	0	7.33
$[f(R_p) - f(R_w)]/c$		$A_3 = 0$	$B_3 = 0$	$C_3 = 14.7$
		$\Sigma A = 17.5$	$\Sigma B = 14.84$	$\Sigma C = 19.27$

Note: A_2, and A_3 and B_3 are zero because C.I. Acid Yellow 27 does not absorb at 520 and 620 nm, and C.I. Acid Red 57 does not absorb at 620 nm.

(b) *The pattern to be matched*
From the reflectance curve of the unknown (light grey) pattern, complete the following:
$\lambda_1 = 420$ nm, $R = 9\%$, $f(R_p) = 4.60$, $f(R_p) - f(R_w) = f(R_1) = 4.22$
$\lambda_2 = 520$ nm, $R = 13\%$, $f(R_p) = 2.91$, $f(R_p) - f(R_w) = f(R_2) = 2.84$
$\lambda_3 = 620$ nm, $R = 13.5\%$, $f(R_p) = 2.77$, $f(R_p) - f(R_w) = f(R_3) = 2.74$
    $\Sigma f(R) = 9.80$

(c) Solving Eqn 8.11

This can be done by matrix algebra on a computer if such a facility is available. For hand calculation complete the following steps, which are based on the general solution of Eqn 8.11.

$$-A_2/A_1 = D =$$
$$-A_3/A_1 = E =$$
$$B_2 + DB_1 = F =$$
$$-(B_3 + EB_1)/F = G =$$
$$C_2 + DC_1 = H =$$
$$C_3 + EC_1 + GH = I =$$
$$f(R_2) + Df(R_1) = K =$$
$$f(R_3) + Ef(R_1) + GK = L =$$
$$L/I = c_z =$$
$$(K - Hc_z)/F = c_y =$$
$$[f(R_1) - C_1c_z - B_1c_y]/A_1 = c_x =$$
$$\text{Check } \Sigma Ac_x + \Sigma Bc_y + \Sigma Cc_z = \Sigma f(R)$$

In this particular case, D, E and G are zero, because A_2, A_3 and B_3 are zero and Eqn 8.11 can be solved readily by hand. For the above data the solution is:

c_x (yellow) = 0.220%
c_y (red)   = 0.159%
c_z (blue)   = 0.186%.

8.4 FOLLOWING DYE UPTAKE FROM A BINARY MIXTURE
(see section 11.7)

Rate of dyeing curves published by the dyestuff manufacturers are often in the form of percentage exhaustion versus a time/temperature axis; for direct dyes on cellulose these curves usually also indicate the influence of the addition of electrolyte. These curves are based on spectrophotometric measurements of the dyebath during dyeing of the single dyes under defined dyeing conditions. In this experiment the rate of dyeing of a pair of direct dyes is followed by spectrophotometry at two wavelengths, using similar principles to that used in the experiment in section 8.3. However, the calculations are much simpler. The absorption curves only partially overlap, as illustrated Figure 8.1.

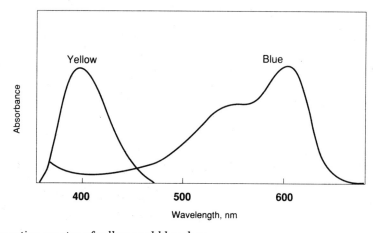

Figure 8.1 – Absorption spectra of yellow and blue dyes

Measurements at 605 nm give the blue directly and hence by proportion its contribution at 395 nm can be calculated.

Assuming the conditions quoted in Table 8.3 apply, by proportion x is calculated as $(0.1/1.0) \times 0.5 = 0.05$. The absorbance due to yellow is then given by $A_y = A_{395} - x$ Using this type of analysis the absorbance values of the mixture can be used to measure blue and yellow dye exhaustions.

Note that since one of the absorption coefficients is zero it is not necessary to solve simultaneous equations in this case.

TABLE 8.3

Dye	Absorbance at	
	605 nm	395 nm
Blue dye alone	1.0	0.1
Blue dye in mixture	0.5	x

Procedure

1. Solutions of the two dyes to be used should be prepared:
   (a) C.I. Direct Blue 218, 6 g/l
   (b) C.I. Direct Yellow 44, 2 g /l.
2. Using these solutions prepare a dyebath for 5 g of unmercerised cotton yarn or fabric with the recipe shown in Table 8.4. Start the dyeing at 40°C, raise the temperature to 95°C over 30 min taking samples as in 3 below, add the Glauber's salt and dye at 95°C for a further 30 min.
3. Remove approx. 3 ml aliquots from the dyebath at the following time intervals: 0, 2, 10, 20, 30 (before salt addition), 45 and 60 min. Cool and dilute 2 ml of each aliquot to 25 ml and measure the absorbance of the diluted samples in 10 mm cells on a suitable spectrophotometer at both 395 and 605 nm.
4. Dilute the stock solution of the blue dye by taking a 5 ml portion and diluting to 500 ml with water and measure at 395 and 605 nm in 10 mm cells.

TABLE 8.4

	Amount (% o.w.f.)
C.I. Direct Blue 218	3
C.I. Direct Yellow 44	1
Glauber's salt	20

Liquor ratio 30:1

Results

1. From the readings of the diluted dyebath samples at 605 nm calculate the percentage of the blue dye left in solution at different times; hence plot percentage exhaustion against time.
2. Use the measurements obtained in 4 to calculate the proportionate contribution (F) for the blue dye at 395 nm.
3. Using this proportionate factor for the blue dye (e.g. $F = 0.1$ in the above example), construct a table of results, as shown in Table 8.5. Hence plot percentage exhaustion of the yellow dye against time.
4. Compare your experimental dye uptake curves (time–temperature–salt curves) with those given in the dye manufacturer's handbook.

TABLE 8.5

Time	0 min
A_{395}	1.0
A_{605}	0.6
$x = F \times A_{605}$	0.06
$A_y = A_{395} - x$	0.94
Yellow	$(A_y/0.94) \times 100\%$
Exhaustion	0%

8.5 STANDARD AFFINITY AND ENTHALPY OF A DISPERSE DYE ON CELLULOSE ACETATE
(see section 10.3)

Standard affinity
When dyeing has proceeded to true equilibrium the fibre will be completely and uniformly penetrated, and adsorption and desorption of dye will be taking place at the same rate. The chemical potential of the dye in the fibre phase (μ_f) is the same as that in the solution phase (μ_s), and there is no net transfer of dye from one phase to the other. However, because the dye has greater affinity for the fibre than for the external solution, the concentration, $[D]_f$, of dye in the fibre is greater than that in the external (dyebath) solution, $[D]_s$. The standard affinity ($-\Delta\mu^\circ$) of a dye for a fibre is derived by equating the chemical potentials as in Eqn 8.12:

$$\mu^\circ_f + RT \ln[D]_f = \mu^\circ_s + RT \ln[D]_s \qquad (8.12)$$

or Eqn 8.13:

$$\Delta\mu^\circ = -RT \ln \frac{[D]_f}{[D]_s} \qquad (8.13)$$

where μ° = standard chemical potential
R = gas constant
T = absolute temperature.

In the simplest case, where the dye is unionised in both phases, e.g. with disperse dyes applied to secondary cellulose acetate from an aqueous dyebath, $[D]_f/[D]_s$ is the partition coefficient K. Thus Eqn 8.14 can be written:

$$- \Delta \mu ° = RT \ln K \qquad (8.14)$$

In the experiment that follows the affinity of a disperse dye for secondary cellulose acetate at a given temperature is determined by measuring the partition coefficient of the dye between the fibre and water at equilibrium, using a desorption technique.

Heat of dyeing

The standard affinity of a dye is dependent on temperature and usually decreases as the temperature rises, i.e. the equilibrium shifts in favour of the solution phase.

When $-\Delta\mu°/T$ is plotted against $1/T$, where T is the absolute temperature $(T = t°C + 273)$, the slope of the straight line obtained gives $\Delta H°$, the heat of dyeing. This thermodynamic parameter is more accurately expressed as the standard enthalpy change associated with the dyeing process, and to an approximation may be considered as a measure of the strength of the net attraction between dye and fibre. If values for $-\Delta\mu°$ or K are available for two temperatures only, it is more convenient to use Eqn 8.15:

$$\Delta H° = \left(\frac{\Delta\mu°_1}{T_1} - \frac{\Delta\mu°_2}{T_2} \right) / \left(\frac{1}{T_1} - \frac{1}{T_2} \right) = \frac{2.3\,RT_1T_2}{T_1 - T_2} \log \frac{K_1}{K_2} \qquad (8.15)$$

The values obtained are usually negative, which indicates that dyeing is an exothermic process.

Procedure

Use a 1 g hank of secondary cellulose acetate fibre and dye in a dyebath containing 5% C.I. Disperse Yellow 3 at a liquor ratio of 80:1 for 2 h at 80°C. On completion of dyeing rinse the dyed material with several changes of cold water. Cut the hank (as accurately as possible) in half. Treat each portion in separate conical flasks containing 80 ml of deionised water, and fitted with thimble condensers for 12 h at 60° and 80°C respectively, with, if possible, continuous agitation. At the end of the prescribed time remove the hanks, rinse with cold water (deionised), squeeze and transfer each sample to a 100 ml graduated flask half filled with acetone. Once the fibre has dissolved, make up the volume with acetone.

Prepare a calibration curve using 5, 10, 20 and 30 mg/l solutions of C.I. Disperse Yellow 3 in acetone in 1 cm cells. Cover the cells to prevent evaporation of the solvent and measure the absorbances at 400 nm.

Determine the absorbance of the acetone solution of each dissolved hank and hence estimate the concentration of dye in each hank, expressed as mg/kg. Calculate the concentration of dye in each desorption solution as mg of dye per litre of solution.

Results

1. Calculate the partition coefficient for C.I. Disperse Yellow 3 between cellulose acetate and water, and hence the standard affinity $(-\Delta\mu°)$ of the dye at the two temperatures.

2. Calculate the enthalpy or heat of dyeing ($\Delta H°$) for the C.I. Disperse Yellow 3/cellulose acetate system.
3. Compare your results with published figures [3].

8.6 THE MECHANISM OF CARRIER DYEING OF DISPERSE DYES ON POLYESTER
(see section 9.5 and ref.4.)

By comparison with other materials used in the textile industry, polyester is one of the most difficult to dye because of the fibre's highly compact and crystalline structure. One method of increasing dye uptake is to dye above the glass-transition temperature (T_g) of the polymer. The T_g is the temperature at which there is a sudden marked increase in free volume within the polymer. Below the T_g the only motions of the polymer chain are thermal vibrations, but increasing the temperature to T_g eventually provides enough energy for bond rotation to occur in the chain. At this point a whole segment between two simultaneously rotating bonds changes position until sterically halted by the other components of the chain. This is referred to as a segmental jump and is indicated by plasticisation or softening of the fibre. Dye adsorption is greatly increased at T_g mainly because of increased accessibility of the dye molecules to the internal regions of the polymer.

Polyester is soluble in phenol, and a number of substituted phenols. Addition to the dyebath of controlled amounts of these and other compounds (known as carriers) substantially reduces the T_g, probably by weakening the bonding forces between the polymer chains.

Accurate T_g values are extremely difficult to measure because they usually occur over a range of temperatures. The following experiment allows a dyeing transition temperature to be obtained, which is a reasonable approximation to T_g.

Procedure
Dye four pieces of polyester fabric as shown in Table 8.6. Enter the wetted out pieces of fabric at the temperature shown and dye for 10 min then remove, soap, rinse and dry.

Repeat the above procedures using the same quantities of dye and phenol and fresh pieces of fabric at dyeing temperatures of 60, 80 and 100°C.

Measure the reflectance of each of the 16 samples at 535 nm, then using the Kubelka–Munk equation (Eqn 8.4) convert R to K/S. Plot K/S versus temperature curves for each concentration of phenol used.

TABLE 8.6

	Amount (% o.w.f.)			
	I	II	III	IV
C.I. Disperse Red 15	4	4	4	4
Phenol (g/l)		10	20	30

Liquor ratio 50:1
Temperature 40°C

Results

1. Extrapolate the straight line portion of each K/S vs temperature curve to the x-axis, and read off the dyeing transition temperature.
2. Assess and comment upon the effect that the increase in phenol concentration has on the dyeing transition temperature and hence on the activation energy of dyeing [4].

8.7 DETERMINATION OF TIME OF HALF DYEING AND OF THE ACTIVATION ENERGY OF DIFFUSION OF A DIRECT DYE IN CELLULOSE

(see section 10.2)

Time of half dyeing ($t_{1/2}$), i.e. the time taken for a fibre to absorb 50% of the dye it will absorb at equilibrium, provides an indirect measure of the rate of dye diffusion within a fibre and is useful for comparing the behaviour of a range of dyes applied under identical conditions. The amount of dye absorbed at equilibrium can be estimated readily and $t_{1/2}$ is then determined using the plot of dye exhaustion versus time of dyeing.

In practice, the experimental conditions must be chosen with care. If these are such that the bulk of the dye is adsorbed on the surface of the fibres very quickly, i.e. if there is rapid 'strike', this will mask the effect of diffusion into the fibre. Conditions should therefore be chosen which ensure that dye–fibre attraction is low and the final exhaustion is about 50%.

The rate of diffusion of a dye in a fibre increases with increase in dyeing temperature and the effect can be expressed quantitatively by Eqn 8.16:

$$\log D_T = -\frac{E}{2.3RT} + a \qquad (8.16)$$

where D_T = the diffusion coefficient at temperature, T
R = gas constant (8.314 J/(K mol))
E = activation energy of diffusion, J/mol
T = temperature, K
a = constant.

Diffusion coefficients and hence activation energies of diffusion are difficult to measure but a corresponding 'activation energy of dyeing' (E_D) can be obtained from rate-of-dyeing measurements, i.e. by plotting $\log t_{1/2}$ against $1/T$. These values are not as fundamental as those based on direct measurement of diffusion, but nevertheless they are valuable as they provide a measure of the effect of temperature on practical dyeing rate. The following experiment illustrates how the time of half dyeing and activation energy of dyeing of a direct dye on cotton can be evaluated.

Procedure

1. Prepare twelve dyebaths as shown in Table 8.7 using twelve 5 g cotton skeins.
2. Carry out six dyeings at 90°C and six at 50°C. Dye each for 0.5, 2, 5, 10, 60 min and 24 h respectively, ensuring constant volume of dyebath (with continued topping up) and constant agitation. Retain the exhausted dyebaths. Assume the 24 h dyeing represents the equilibrium exhaustion at each temperature.
3. Prepare a calibration plot (absorbance vs concentration) using standard solutions of 10, 20, 30 and 40 mg/l C.I. Direct Red 81. Measurements should be made at 540 nm (λ_{max}) in 10 mm cells.
4. Using this calibration plot, and by suitable dilution as required, estimate the concentrations of dye in each of the exhaust dyebaths, and hence percentage exhaustions.

TABLE 8.7

	Amount (% o.w.f.)
C.I. Direct Red 81	1
Sodium chloride	5

Liquor ratio 25:1

Results
1. Plot percentage exhaustion vs time at the two temperatures and read off the $t_{1/2}$ values from these plots. (In certain cases it is preferable to plot exhaustion vs log t since the relevant portion tends to be a straight line and a more accurate estimate of $t_{1/2}$ can be obtained.)
2. The 'activation energy of dyeing'(E_D) is calculated from Eqn 8.17:

$$\log(t_{1/2})_{323} - \log(t_{1/2})_{363} = \frac{E_D}{2.3R}\left[\frac{363 - 323}{363 \times 323}\right] \qquad (8.17)$$

3. Compare the result you obtain with those given in the literature [5].

8.8 DETERMINATION OF THE DIFFUSION COEFFICIENT OF A DISPERSE DYE IN NYLON 6.6 FILM
(see section 10.2)
Diffusion of a dye into fibre-forming material of known thickness from an 'infinite' dyebath (i.e. one in which no appreciable change in concentration of dye occurs during dyeing) conforms to Hill's equation. This equation applies to dye diffusion into an infinitely long cylinder, which in effect corresponds to a textile fibre, and can be expressed in the form of an infinite series (Eqn 8.18):

$$\frac{c_t}{c_\infty} = 1 - Ae^{-By} - Ce^{-Ey} \; \dots \qquad (8.18)$$

where c_t = concentration of dye in the fibre at time t
c_∞ = concentration of dye in the fibre at equilibrium
y = Dt/r^2
D = diffusion coefficient of the dye
r = radius of fibre
$A, B, C, E,$ etc. = constants.

c_t/c_∞ is thus related to Dt/r^2. This expression can be utilised for a film as well as a fibre (with thickness l replacing r).
    Solutions of this type of equation are provided in the form of tables (see Table 8.8). Thus the apparent diffusion coefficient of a dye in a fibre or film can be determined. A small mass of the material is dyed in a large volume of dye solution for a prolonged time and the amount of dye absorbed is determined to give the value c_∞. Another dyeing is then carried out for

a much shorter time, t, and c_t determined. The value c_t/c_∞ is calculated, and the corresponding value Dt/l^2 read off, and, since l and t are known, D can be calculated. Repetition of the experiment using different dyeing times indicates the constancy of D and the validity of the equation.

TABLE 8.8

c_t/c_∞	Dt/l^2	c_t/c_∞	Dt/l^2	c_t/c_∞	Dt/l^2
0.980	0.40	0.666	0.09	0.215	0.009
0.958	0.30	0.631	0.08	0.202	0.008
0.887	0.20	0.593	0.07	0.189	0.007
0.816	0.15	0.552	0.06	0.176	0.006
0.796	0.14	0.504	0.05	0.159	0.005
0.776	0.13	0.450	0.04	0.142	0.004
0.752	0.12	0.391	0.03	0.124	0.003
0.729	0.11	0.319	0.02	0.102	0.002
0.698	0.10	0.225	0.01	0.071	0.001

Procedure
Prepare three dyebaths of identical composition containing 1 g C.I. Disperse Red 11 and 2 ml Matexil DN-VL (ICI) in 160 ml of liquor. Dye a 0.1 g piece of nylon film of known thickness (l) in each of the three dyebaths at 80°C for 10 min, 20 min and 24 h respectively, ensuring that the film is suspended in such a way that it is in minimum contact with anything other than the dye dispersion, and under constant agitation. At the end of these dyeing times rinse the film with deionised water and dry. Dissolve the dyed film in approx. 20 ml boiling dimethylformamide (DMF), taking great care. Rapidly cool and filter carefully to remove the precipitated nylon. Wash the nylon carefully several times with hot DMF at about 70°C. Transfer the combined filtrate to a 50 ml graduated flask (100 ml in the case of the 24 h dyeing) and make up the volume with DMF. Prepare a calibration curve (absorbance vs concentration) using solutions containing 20, 40, 60 and 100 mg/l dye in DMF. Measurements should be made at 535 nm (λ_{max}) in 10 mm cells. Determine the concentration of dye in each of the extracts and hence calculate the amount of dye which has diffused into each of the films. The value for the 24 h dyeing should be taken as a measure of c_∞.

Results
1. Use the results obtained to calculate c_t/c_∞ for t = 10 min and t = 20 min.
2. From Table 8.8 read off the the values of Dt/l^2 corresponding to the two c_t/c_∞ values.
3. Using the known values of l (cm) and t (s), calculate the diffusion coefficient of C.I. Disperse Red 11 in nylon in units of cm²/s.
4. By reference to the literature [6,7], students should comment on the use of Hill's equation and the related McBain's equation for the evaluation of the diffusion coefficients of dyes.

8.9 EXPERIMENTS ON COLOUR MEASUREMENT
(see sections 12.1–12.5)

General
A significant development in recent years in the colour-manufacturing and colour-using industries has been the adoption of instrumental methods of colour measurement and specification for colour control, colour sorting and colour match prediction. This development is a result of improved instrumentation, on-line microcomputing facilities and rapid data analysis procedures. Most colour measurements are based on the initial determination of the CIE tristimulus values (X, Y and Z) with subsequent mathematical conversion to quantities which correlate with visual assessments of the colour or the colour difference.

Colour specifications are three-dimensional, but traditionally it has been the practice to show hue and chroma variations on a two-dimensional chromaticity diagram with the lightness measurement given separately. This can be done by using the CIE 1931 (xy) diagram or the CIELAB 1976 (a*b*) coordinate system.

The specification of colour differences requires the use of the CIELAB (L*a*b*) coordinates, with the total colour difference between two samples given by Eqn 8.19:

$$\Delta E = [(L^*_1 - L^*_2)^2 + (a^*_1 - a^*_2)^2 + (b^*_1 - b^*_2)^2]^{1/2} \tag{8.19}$$

This can be resolved into three polar coordinate differences (ΔL^*, ΔC^* and ΔH^*) which correlate respectively with the lightness, chroma and hue differences between the samples.

Three short experiments are described here to illustrate:
(a) The computation of CIE XYZ values
(b) The specification of the colour gamut of a three-dye mixture
(c) The measurement of colour differences.

Experiment (a): CIE tristimulus values
The standard method of specifying colours was introduced by the Commission Internationale de l'Éclairage (CIE) in 1931 and defines colour in terms of three tristimulus values X, Y and Z, which for opaque surface colours are best regarded as giving approximate measures of reflectance of light in the red, green and blue regions of the spectrum respectively. Various methods of evaluating the XYZ values are available, but the most fundamental method is based on Eqns 8.20–8.22, which are summed over the visible spectrum, i.e. 400–700 nm:

$$X = \sum R(\lambda)S(\lambda)\bar{x}(\lambda) \tag{8.20}$$

$$Y = \sum R(\lambda)S(\lambda)\bar{y}(\lambda) \tag{8.21}$$

$$Z = \sum R(\lambda)S(\lambda)\bar{z}(\lambda) \tag{8.22}$$

where $R(\lambda)$ = spectral reflectance of the coloured surface
$S(\lambda)$ = spectral power distribution of a chosen illuminant
$\bar{x}(\lambda)$, $\bar{y}(\lambda)$ and $\bar{z}(\lambda)$ = colour matching functions of a standard observer.

Nowadays we have the choice of the 2° (1931) standard observer, or the 10° (1964) standard observer, while for illuminants the 1931 choice of types A, B or C has been supplemented by the 1967 choice of D_{55}, D_{65} or D_{75}. In the present experiment we compute the results for the 10° (1964) standard observer, for both illuminant A (tungsten light) and illuminant D_{65} (standard artificial daylight).

Procedure
1. Set up the recording spectrophotometer for reflectance measurements as instructed and check the reflectance of the white reference over the visible region (400–700 nm).
2. If the system allows automatic computation of CIE values then check that the results for the white reference (e.g. pressed barium sulphate) are close to the values given in Table 8.9.

TABLE 8.9

	X	Y	Z
Illuminant D_{65}	93	98	105
Illuminant A	109	98	34

3. Choose a coloured sample to be measured (this may also be used for the experiment in section 8.10) and measure its reflectance over the range 400–700 nm, noting the reflectance values ($R\%$) at 20 nm intervals (16 in all).
4. Tabulate the $R\%$ values as shown in Table 8.10 and carry out the multiplications and summations (as illustrated for the value of a typical grey surface) to give the XYZ values of the chosen pattern using the data in Table 8.11. If possible the results should be compared with those given by the computer.
5. If you have access to computerised methods of CIE evaluation, determine also the values of XYZ under 10°/illuminant A conditions [8].

Experiment (b): Colour gamut and colour maps
The range of colours obtained from a mixture of dyes can be illustrated in chromaticity diagrams, provided we recognise that these are only two-dimensional and that the colour gamut depends on the concentration at which the dye is applied. In the experiment below we record the gamut of three level-dyeing acid dyes on wool at 0.5% total fixed concentration. Other concentration levels can be tried to build up a series of two-dimensional gamuts at a range of concentration levels. It is suggested that both 1931 (xy) and 1976 (a^*b^*) plots are used.

Procedure
1. Red, yellow and blue levelling acid dyes should be chosen (preferably those to be used in the experiment in section 8.10), and dyeings of the single dyes and two-dye mixtures prepared at 0.5% strength. Three binary mixtures are suggested at 0.12/0.38%, 0.25/0.25% and 0.38/0.12% strength for each pair of dyes in turn (nine binary dyeings plus three single-dye dyeings).
2. The XYZ values for illuminant D_{65} and the 10° standard observer should be measured for all twelve dyeings and converted as in Eqn 8.23–8.26 to xy and a^*b^* coordinates:

$$x = \frac{X}{X + Y + Z} \tag{8.23}$$

TABLE 8.10

Computation of CIE values ($D_{65}/10°$) for a grey (Z value only shown)

λ (nm)	$S_\lambda \bar{z}_\lambda$	R (%)	Product
400	1.0906	9.5	10.36
420	15.3824	11.0	169.21
440	34.3830	14.2	488.24
460	35.3562	18.6	651.62
480	15.8979	20.0	317.95
500	3.9972	18.1	72.35
520	1.0457	16.0	16.73
540	0.2373	15.5	3.68
560	0.0025	16.1	0.04
580	-0.0022	18.0	−0.04
600	0.0000	19.0	0.000
620	0.0000	19.8	0.000
640	0.0000	20.1	0.000
660	0.0000	24.2	0.000
680	0.0000	35.1	0.000
700	0.0000	51.2	0.000
			$\Sigma = 1736$

i.e. $Z = 1736/100 = 17.36$

Note: The sum of the products should be divided by 100, since the reflectance is given as a percentage. Students can check the method by evaluating X and Y values using $S_\lambda \bar{x}_\lambda$ and $S_\lambda \bar{y}_\lambda$ values given in Table 8.10 (for the above grey $X = 17.00$ and $Y = 17.39$)

$$y = \frac{Y}{X + Y + Z} \tag{8.24}$$

$$a* = 500 \left| \left(\frac{X}{93} \right)^{1/3} - \left(\frac{Y}{98} \right)^{1/3} \right| \tag{8.25}$$

$$b* = 200 \left[\left(\frac{Y}{98} \right)^{1/3} - \left(\frac{Z}{105} \right)^{1/3} \right] \tag{8.26}$$

For reference white, $X_0 = 93$, $Y_0 = 98$, $Z_0 = 105$ have been used (see Eqn 2.2–2.4).

Results
1. Plots of the single dyes and mixtures should be shown in xy and $a*b*$ coordinates and the colour gamuts (triangles) compared. (c.f. section 3.5).
2. Show that the coordinates of ternary dyeings lie within the colour gamut (e.g. the samples measured in experiment (a)).

TABLE 8.11

Data for computation of CIE values ($D_{65}/10°$)

λ (nm)	$S_\lambda \bar{x}_\lambda$	$S_\lambda \bar{y}_\lambda$	$S_\lambda \bar{z}_\lambda$
400	0.2516	0.0236	1.0906
420	3.2317	0.3301	15.3824
440	6.6805	1.1069	34.3830
460	6.0964	2.6206	35.3562
480	1.7213	4.9378	15.8979
500	0.0589	8.6695	3.9972
520	2.1845	13.8473	1.0457
540	6.8093	17.3537	0.2373
560	12.1626	17.1539	0.0025
580	16.4686	14.1481	-0.0022
600	17.2340	10.1056	0.0000
620	12.8953	6.0212	0.0000
640	6.2267	2.5867	0.0000
660	2.1113	0.8268	0.0000
680	0.5736	0.2222	0.0000
700	0.1209	0.0460	0.0000

Experiment (c): Colour difference

Colour-difference evaluation requires the use of the three coordinates of an approximately visually uniform colour space (e.g. CIELAB 1976), as discussed above. In this experiment either the colour differences of a metameric series of patterns are evaluated under different light sources, or the colour changes produced by a standard wash test are measured.

Procedure

If computer colour matching experiments (e.g. section 8.10) are carried out regularly then a standard pattern and, say, two matched patterns using different dye combinations should be available. These will form a metameric set to be used as described below to assess the colour differences. Alternatively two dyed samples (e.g. different ternary mixtures on wool) should be cut in half, and one half of each subjected to a standard wash test (e.g. ISO2 or C02) and the originals and washed samples used as described below to assess colour differences.

1. Measure the *XYZ* values of the standards and the samples on a suitable instrument (either a colorimeter or a spectrophotometer). If possible measurements should be made for both daylight (D_{65}) and tungsten light (A) illuminants.
2. Convert the *XYZ* readings to the coordinates of a suitable uniform colour space (e.g ANLAB(40) or CIELAB 1976)[1].

---

1. ANLAB(40) calculations, see J.S.D.C., **86** (1970) 354.
CIELAB (1976) calculations are based on:
$L^* = 116 (Y/98)^{1/3} - 16$
a^* and b^* defined as above

3. Evaluate the total colour difference (ΔE) in the coordinates chosen, if possible, for the two illuminant conditions.
4. Assess the samples visually under the two illuminants and give full descriptions of the colour differences observed, e.g. describe differences in the dyer's terminology of hue, strength and dullness/brightness (see sections 2.3 and 12.2).
5. (a) For the metameric samples class the degree of metamerism as low, medium or high[1].
   (b) For the washed samples visually assess the colour differences against the grey scale for assessing the change of colour of the pattern.

Results
1. Tabulate the visual and numerical colour differences and comment on their relationship.
2. (a) For the metameric samples, evaluate a metameric index $(MI) = \Delta E(A) - \Delta E(D_{65})$ and compare with the visual assessments of metamerism.
   (b) For the washed samples, compare the visual grey scale evaluations with these predicted from the measured $\Delta E(D_{65})$ values, with the help of Table 8.12.

TABLE 8.12

Grey scale grade	ΔE	
	ANLAB(40)	CIELAB
5	0	0
4	1.5	1.7
3	3.0	3.4
2	6.0	6.8
1	12.0	13.6

Other relevant experiments
Some other experiments which might be added to the above list include:
(i)   Assessment of whiteness in bleached and FBA-treated samples (whiteness index)
(ii) Assessment of yellowing of whites using a yellowness index
(iii) Assessment of colour vision tests
(iv) Following colour changes of standards and samples during light fastness tests.

8.10 COMPUTER COLOUR MATCHING (INSTRUMENTAL MATCH PREDICTION)
Most manufacturers of coloured goods face the problem of producing their products to a colour specification defined by their customer, usually by means of a physical sample or standard. The traditional method of colour matching in the dyeing, paint and plastics industries was to prepare in the laboratory, by trial and error methods, a small sample which was judged visually to be a good colour match to the submitted standard. This laboratory sample was then used as the basis for the bulk production.

---

1. The Davidson and Hemmendinger (D & H) Color Rule is used for assessing observers and illuminants. Assume that the colour change of the rule under D_{65}/A illuminant change illustrates a high degree of metamerism.

In recent years the trial and error method based on visual assessment has been replaced by computer colour matching or instrumental match prediction procedures operated in the producers' plant or provided as a service by most dye and pigment manufacturers. The technique is usually based on the calculation of reflectance data using previously determined calibration coefficients for the dyes or pigments to be used, and comparing the predicted XYZ values with those of the sample to be matched. An outline of the procedure is represented by Figure 8.2.

In the present experiment a computer colour matching program written in BASIC is provided (Appendix B). This utilises calibration data determined for three level-dyeing acid dyes on wool based on the Kubelka–Munk analysis of reflectance data (section 8.2). In the present version of the program the values of c_1, c_2 and c_3 along with the corresponding XYZ values are printed at every cycle in the iteration up to ten cycles, with the correction coefficients being available if required at the end.

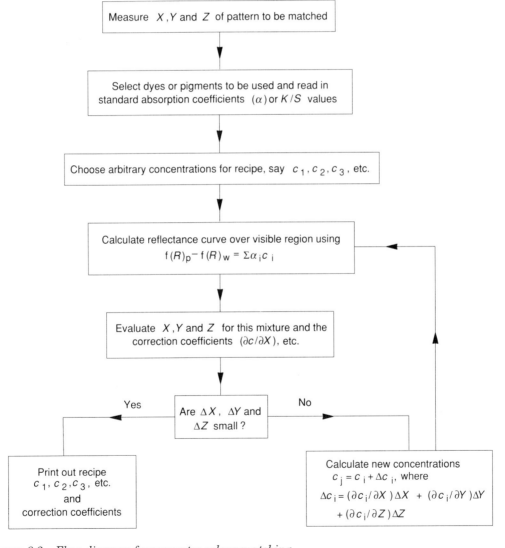

Figure 8.2 – Flow diagram for computer colour matching

The program may require some modification to run on the particular computer system available, and this should be checked beforehand.

Procedure

1. Choose a pattern to be matched, preferably either a piece of grey card or a previous ternary dyeing using the dyes specified in the program.
2. By suitable methods determine the XYZ values of the pattern under illuminant D_{65} and $10°$ standard observer conditions (experiment (a) in section 8.9). This should be done preferably by recording the reflectance spectrum, which should be retained for comparison with that for the dyeing based on the computer calculated recipe.
3. Submit the XYZ values in the computer program, utilising arbitrary starting concentrations of $c_1 = c_2 = c_3 = 0.1\%$.
4. If a negative concentration is obtained and the program fails, try altering the starting concentrations, e.g. to 0.01 or 0.5% as appropriate. If this fails the sample chosen must lie outside the gamut of the level-dyeing acid dyes used in the calibration data. (This should not happen for a grey card or a known ternary dyeing.)
5. Using the computer calculated recipe figures (which are based on percentage of dye on weight of fibre) calculate the volumes of suitable stock dye solutions (e.g. 1 g/l) to be used to dye an appropriate weight of scoured wool cloth (e.g. 2.5 or 5.0 g). Dye using the three dye solutions as calculated plus sulphuric acid (3%) and sodium sulphate (20%) at a liquor ratio of 50:1. Start dyeing at $40°C$, enter the scoured and wetted wool, raise to $95°C$, and dye for 20–30 min at $95°C$. Remove the sample, rinse in cold water and dry.
6. Record the reflectance spectrum of the matched sample on the same chart as used for the unknown in 2. above. Evaluate the XYZ and ΔE values for both illuminant D_{65} and illuminant A (experiment (c) in section 8.9).

Results

1. Mount the samples and original pattern side by side and comment on the closeness of match under tungsten and (simulated) daylight conditions.
2. Comment on any metamerism present in terms of the recorded spectra and visual assessments.
3. Tabulate the colour-difference values under illuminants A and D_{65}, and evaluate the metameric index, if appropriate.
4. Comment on the number of iterations required to give the final recipe to sufficient precision.

REFERENCES

1. E I Stearns, 'The practice of absorption spectrophotometry' (New York: Wiley Interscience, 1969).
2. 'Colour physics for industry', Ed. R McDonald (Bradford: Dyers' Company Publications Trust, 1987) 30.
3. C L Bird and P Harris, J.S.D.C., **73** (1957) 199.
4. W Ingamells and R H Peters, J.S.D.C., **89** (1973) 397.
5. F Jones in 'Theory of coloration of textiles', Ed. C L Bird and W S Boston (Bradford: Dyers' Company Publications Trust, 1975) 255, 281.
6. T Vickerstaff, 'The physical chemistry of dyeing' (London: Oliver and Boyd, 1954).
7. 'Theory of coloration of textiles', Ed. C L Bird and W S Boston (Bradford: Dyers' Company Publications Trust, 1975).
8. 'Colour physics for industry', Ed. R McDonald (Bradford: Dyers' Company Publications Trust, 1987) 290.

PART III

Theoretical considerations

9 CHEMISTRY OF DYES AND FIBRES

9.1 HISTORY AND DEVELOPMENT

Dyeing is one of the most ancient crafts and its history can be traced back at least 4000 years. It demanded a high degree of skill and details of the methods used by dyers were jealously guarded.

Until the middle of the last century all dyes were natural products, extracted in most cases from a variety of plants, but also from a few animal sources. The roots, stems, leaves, flowers and fruits of various plants supplied reds, yellows, browns, blues, blacks and, from animal sources, important reds were obtained from extracts of certain dried insects. The famous Tyrian purple was produced from molluscs found on the shores of the Mediterranean Sea.

Fibres were also natural products and were either cellulosic (linen and cotton) or protein (wool, silk and various hair fibres). The dyes were applied in many cases with the aid of a so-called mordant, an inorganic salt able to combine with the dye and improve its fixation to the fibre, though usually at the expense of some loss of brightness in the colour. Alum or salts of iron, copper or tin were the common mordants. Chromium salts, which are now used almost exclusively, did not come into prominence until about the middle of the 19th century.

Mixing blue, yellow and red to produce any desired hue is usually considered a development of modern times made necessary by the use of colour in printing and photography as well as in dyeing. This belief needs re-evaluation since the recent discovery of wool goods 2000 years old on which different fast dyeings, including blacks, had been prepared with mixtures of indigo, saffron (for yellow) and red dyes prepared from madder root skilfully mordanted with blends of alum and iron salts according to the desired colour. This is by no means the earliest example of fast dyeing. We read in Exodus that more than a thousand years earlier it was recorded 'ye shall take of them... blue, and purple and scarlet and fine linen and goats' hair, and rams' skins dyed red...'. These colours probably refer to indigo, the dye now known as Tyrian purple, and kermes, the products respectively of a plant (one of the *Indigofera* species), a mollusc (one of several species of the genera *Murex* and *Purpura*) and a dried insect (*Kermes ilicis*). Fabrics found in the tombs of ancient Egypt reveal that the craft of dyeing was known at least as early as 2500 BC. It is believed to have originated in India (cf. the name indigo) and to have spread westward to Persia, Phoenicia and Egypt.

Apart from the introduction of chromium salts as mordants about 1850, little fundamental change in old-established methods of dyeing occurred until the synthetic dyes prepared from coal-tar products appeared after 1856. The mid-19th century was a time of great advances in the understanding of organic chemistry and the work of academic and industrial scientists went hand in hand as the new dyestuffs industry emerged. In 1858 Kekulé and Couper independently postulated the tetravalency of carbon. Seven years later Kekulé put forward his cyclic structure for benzene, while other leading chemists made significant contributions during this period. Thus Hofmann isolated benzene from coal tar,

Griess discovered the diazo reaction, and the syntheses of alizarin and indigo were accomplished by Graebe and Liebermann, and von Baeyer respectively, all within a relatively short space of time. But this alliance between pure science and industry is best symbolised by the astonishing achievement in 1856 of W H Perkin, who as a student at the Royal College of Chemistry in London accidentally prepared a violet substance that proved to be an excellent dye. He was a youth of 18, but with sufficient courage and initiative to establish the manufacture of the dye and to found what has become one of the great industries of modern times.

Perkin's success in isolating the first synthetic dye from the oxidation products of crude aniline led to a period of intense activity. Thus Perkin's mauveine was followed by the discoveries of dyes like magenta (1859), Hofmann's violet (1863) and many others. These early dyes were cationic in character and possessed little substantivity for cotton, though they gave bright shades on wool and silk. The problem of devising a method suitable for application to cotton was also solved by the young Perkin who used tannic acid as a mordant to precipitate the basic dyes in the fibre in an insoluble form.

The discovery of the diazo reaction in the early 1860s by Peter Griess, a chemist in a brewery at Burton-on-Trent, laid the foundation for the manufacture of azo dyes and pigments which today account for more than 50% of all colorants. The full commercial exploitation of this discovery took over ten years and early azo dyes were mainly of yellow and orange hues. The subsequent discovery by Böttiger in 1884 that the disazo dye Congo red – containing sulphonic acid groups to confer water solubility – could be applied to cotton directly and without a mordant, resulted in the manufacture during the following decade of a large number of so-called 'direct' dyes based on the diamine benzidine.

In 1893 the first sulphur black was prepared and many other insoluble dyes of this type soon followed, prepared by heating aromatic amines and phenols with sulphur and applied to cotton from dyebaths containing the reducing agent sodium sulphide. Sulphur dyes have remained to this day the most widely used of all dyes for cellulosics, a measure of their fastness and cheapness. The industrial synthesis of indigo in 1897 and the discovery in 1901 of indanthrene by Bohn gave further impetus to the application of dyes to cotton by reduction–oxidation cycles. Indanthrene itself was the first in a number of vat dyes of outstanding fastness based on anthraquinone. The vat dye range had no bright reds and this gap in fast colours for cotton was filled by the azoic colorants. Though the first recommendation for producing insoluble azo colorants on cotton dates from the 1880s, little progress was made until 1911 when it was discovered that the anilides of 3-hydroxy-2-naphthoic acid as coupling components were substantive to cotton. The particular mode of application of these azoic colorants means that there are large numbers of possible combinations of coupling components and diazo components, though only a few of these are now commercially important. The shade range covered is predominantly red–bordeaux, with yellow and black being important exceptions.

Griess's extensive work in the 1860s on the reactions between aromatic bases and nitrous acid included a patent ('metachrome' patent) in which he showed that the fastness of certain azo dyes based on picramic acid (2-amino-4,6-dinitrophenol) showed improved fastness on wool when applied with a mordant. This led, 30 years later, to the development of chrome dyeing processes where dyeings of the highest fastness were obtained on wool, mordanted with a transition metal (usually chromium) and dyed with azo dyes, typically carrying two hydroxyl groups *ortho* to the azo group or formed from the coupling component salicylic acid. Later still the 1:1 metal-complex dyes were introduced in 1915, and the 1:2 metal-complex dyes 30 years after that. The latter group still retains an important place in the production of fast shades on wool and nylon.

The First World War delayed developments in the industry but by the 1920s there was a trend towards improved fastness and this stimulated renewed interest in anthraquinone vat dyes of greater structural complexity. One important result of this was the discovery by Scottish Dyes of the green vat dye, Caledon Jade Green, one of the outstanding discoveries in colour chemistry. Soon after this Caledon Jade Green and other vat dyes became available commercially in water-soluble forms, these being the sulphuric acid esters of the leuco derivative of the vat dye, and, though expensive, these solublised vat dyes have continued to hold some attraction since the vatting stage is eliminated.

This period also saw the introduction of the synthetic secondary cellulose acetate fibre in which about 2.3 hydroxyl groups per glucose unit in the cellulose were acetylated. The dye classes available at that time were found to be unsuitable for dyeing the new fibre, but research by British chemists resulted in the appearance of a new dye class, the disperse dyes. Thus Holland Ellis of British Celanese Ltd was able to show that fine aqueous dispersions of aminoazobenzene and diphenylamine derivatives could be applied simply and effectively to cellulose diacetate fibres. Up to the present day the disperse dyes remain the most important class of dye not only for secondary cellulose acetate, but for cellulose triacetate and polyester as well. Structurally the dyes are now, for the most part, aminoazobenzene and anthraquinone derivatives containing powerful electron donor and acceptor groups, and the colour gamut of the former type has recently been extended into the blue and green range by the use of diazo components and sometimes coupling components based on heterocycles.

1925 saw one of the great discoveries in the history of colour chemistry. From a reaction vessel in which phthalic anhydride was being converted into phthalimide, chemists at Scottish Dyes Ltd isolated traces of a bright blue impurity. It took some years for the structure of copper phthalocyanine to be elucidated and it turned out to be a colorant of outstanding brilliance and durability. Though not itself a dye, the phthalocyanine chromophore has been exploited by dyestuff chemists to produce blue–turquoise direct, ingrain and reactive (see below) dyes for cellulosic fibres and acid and reactive dyes for wool. The parent pigment is of course the basis of most blue paints, printing inks and plastics.

Since the Second World War the most important development in the dyestuffs industry has been the introduction by ICI in 1956 of Procion reactive dyes for cellulosic fibres. The first three of these marketed were essentially sulphonated azo or anthraquinone acid dye types containing dichlorotriazinyl ring systems. In the presence of alkali, ionised cellulose takes part in a nucleophilic displacement type of reaction at the triazinyl rings with the formation of a covalent dye–fibre bond. Various manufacturers introduced ranges of such dyes soon afterwards in which other heterocycles replaced triazine as the reactive nucleus, while Hoechst's Remazol range contained a reactive group precursor – the sulphuric acid ester of β-hydroxyethylsulphone. Under alkaline conditions the reactive vinylsulphone group is generated and this undergoes a nucleophilic addition reaction with ionised cellulose. The original reactive dyes were particularly suited to continuous dyeing and printing techniques and they still remain popular in these areas, while ranges specially developed for batchwise dyeing have also been introduced.

The application of reactive dyes to wool is less straightforward than it is for cotton despite the fact that the former fibre contains more potential groups for dye–fibre reaction. Ranges of such dyes have, however, appeared in the last 25 years, and these are typified by the Ciba–Geigy Lanasol range which contain a reactive α-bromoacryloylamino group. These are applied under acid conditions and react with the fibre in a reaction analogous to the Michael addition in organic chemistry.

The development of acrylic fibres in the 1950s brought with it the introduction of a new and modified form of basic (cationic) dye. The original dyes of this type, introduced nearly a century earlier, gave an unacceptable degree of fastness on acrylics, where the dye–fibre interactions are thought to be mainly electrostatic and the mechanism of dyeing one of ion exchange at the acidic sites in the fibre. These sites result from the catalysts and/or co-monomers used in the fibre polymerisation process. The modified basic dyes consist of azo and anthraquinone structures containing a quaternised nitrogen usually at the end of a pendant group in the molecule.

Recent times have seen an entrenchment in the dyestuffs industry with the elimination of many dyes in existing ranges and much emphasis being placed on the improvement of synthetic routes to established and profitable members.

The story of the dyestuffs industry and of the men who pioneered its outstanding developments makes fascinating and instructive reading for any student of chemistry.

9.2 COLOUR AND CONSTITUTION

Mauveine, the first aniline dye to be produced commercially, was prepared in 1856 by W H Perkin, by accident, when he was attempting to make a different substance, quinine. Until that time all but a few dyes were obtained direct from natural sources, usually from plants, though some were animal or mineral products. Very few of these natural dyes are still in use, and only one (logwood, C.I. Natural Black 1) is used in any quantity, almost all dyes now being prepared synthetically. Because of the great number of different fibres and other materials which require to be dyed, and the extremely wide variation in the types of wear and tear to which they are subjected, many thousands of different dyes have been made, and the number is constantly increasing.

The four principal properties that dyes must possess are:
(a) Intense colour
(b) In almost all cases, solubility in an aqueous solution (either permanently or only during the dyeing operation)
(c) Ability to be adsorbed on and retained by the fibre (substantivity) or to be chemically combined with it (reactivity)
(d) Fastness, i.e. the ability when attached to a fibre to withstand the treatment the fibre undergoes in manufacturing processes and in normal use.

The dye chemist has to combine suitable groups in an organic molecule to give a product having the most satisfactory combination of these properties for any desired use. The following comments are intended to illustrate how the first of these properties, that of colour, originates in dye molecules.

Ever since Perkin's discovery, dye chemists and others have turned their minds to the establishment of some kind of relationship between the colour of a molecule and its chemical constitution, and this chapter deals briefly with these attempts. Complete coverage of what is a complex topic requires an understanding of theoretical aspects of organic and physical chemistry which are beyond the scope of this book, and students wishing to pursue the subject further are referred to the references and bibliography at the end of the chapter. Although the idea of being able to predict accurately the colour of a molecule from its structure is of course an appealing one to dye chemists, it has to be said that the approach today towards development of new dyes remains in the main one of intuition, experience and empiricism.

Early theories
It is worth remembering that Perkin's mauveine appeared nearly ten years before Kekulé

put forward his cyclic structure for benzene and 40 years before the discovery of the electron. The latter half of the 19th century saw not only large numbers of new dyes produced but also many important developments in structural organic chemistry, and these two facts are not unrelated.

By 1867, however, the yellow *p*-benzoquinone (I) was the only coloured compound the structure of which was known, but in the same year Graebe and Liebermann made the important discovery that the colour of all the dyes known at that time was destroyed by reduction, leading them to the conclusion that coloured molecules were therefore unsaturated.

I

It was another ten years before the first systematic attempt was made to establish the structural requirements for colour in a molecule. The hypothesis of Otto Witt (1876) still forms a useful rule-of-thumb guide to colour–constitution relationships and the terminology he proposed is used today.

He suggested that dyes consisted of:
(a) Unsaturated groups called chromophores
(b) 'Salt-forming' groups called auxochromes.

Among the chromophores known to be present in dyes at the time were the azo, carbonyl, and nitro groups.

When attached to aromatic ring systems the chromophores form (usually) weakly coloured compounds. Thus azobenzene (II) is orange, while anthraquinone (III) and nitrobenzene (IV) are both very pale yellow. The combined unit (chromophore plus aromatic ring system) Witt named a chromogen. Azobenzene, however, is not a dye, which can only be formed by the addition of one or more auxochromes, groups such as OH, NH_2, $NHCH_3$ and $N(CH_3)_2$.

II

III   IV

Witt's theory was applicable to azo dyes and subsequently to quinonoid dyes but could not adequately explain the intense colour associated with the early cationic dyes based on triphenylmethane, such as Doebner's violet (V).

The discovery in 1900 by Gomberg of the triphenylmethyl radical (VI), a coloured species with neither chromogen nor auxochrome, further highlighted the shortcomings of this theory in providing an explanation of colour–structure relationships.

V

VI

Two further interesting empirical observations were made shortly after Witt's theory appeared. In 1879 Nietzki suggested that increasing the molecular weight of a dye by the introduction of groups such as CH_3, C_2H_5, C_6H_5, OC_2H_5 and Br gave rise to a bathochromic (longer wavelength) shift in its absorption spectrum, i.e. gave a darker colour. Some eight years later Armstrong put forward his quinonoid theory suggesting that only compounds which can be written as o- or p-quinonoid structures would show colour. Many exceptions to these empirical theories were found and further progress in this area was hindered by a lack of fundamental understanding of the light absorption process. By the turn of the century the electron had been discovered and major advances made in unravelling the structure of atoms and molecules. Colour was then seen to arise as a result of some form of oscillation within a molecule when that molecule interacted with electromagnetic radiation. Thus von Baeyer (1900–07) suggested that colourless compounds could be rendered coloured on salt formation ('halochromy') and that a cationic dye like V existed as an equilibrium mixture in which the chloride ion flips from one amino group to another, giving rise to an oscillation between quinonoid and aromatic rings.

That these molecular interactions involved electrons was suggested by Adam and Rosenstein who proposed that the colour in phenolphthalein (VII) was due to 'oscillations' between the following two structures.

VII

The earlier theories of Witt and Nietzki were subsequently extended in the light of a greater appreciation of the nature of the electron and its importance in chemical bonding. Thus in 1907 Hewitt and Mitchell realised the importance for colour of conjugation (a system of alternating single and double bonds) and that the darkening of colour was directly related to an increase in the length of the conjugated chain. Some years later Dilthey and Wizinger modified Witt's ideas by proposing that a coloured dye molecule consisted of an electron-releasing basic group (Witt's auxochrome) connected to an electron-withdrawing acidic group through a system of conjugated double bonds. The greater the nucleophilic and electrophilic character of the two groups, and/or the longer the conjugated chain, the greater was the bathochromic shift.

Further developments led to the concept of resonance, whereby a molecule could be written in a number of forms (canonical structures) which differed one from the other only in the arrangement of the mobile π-electrons. None of these structures describes the molecule as it really exists, which may be represented as a hybrid to which these imaginary structures contribute. Thus II(a–e) represent some of the forms contributing to the hybrid of azobenzene (II). Of these (c) is the most stable, because no energy has been required to separate charges and both rings are stabilised by resonance. The function of the auxochromic group is to increase the stability of the alternative configurations; this it does because it can retain a charge more readily than a carbon atom can.

II

For example, when two auxochromic groups are attached to the azobenzene molecule, the alternative electronic configuration II(f) is more stable than (a), (b), (d) or (e) because the charges may now be held on the oxygen atoms, which can retain them more readily. The result is that compound II(f) has a more intense colour than azobenzene.

II(f)

With an increase in stability of the contributing electronic structure of a molecule, its electrons may be considered to move more readily along the chromophore. Thus the natural frequency of its vibration is decreased. There is a simple analogy with a violin string; the longer the string, the lower is the frequency and hence the longer is the wavelength of the note it emits when plucked, i.e. the wavelength increases with the length of the oscillator. This applies to absorption as well as emission of energy, whether it be sound energy or light energy, because any oscillator absorbs energy most readily at the wavelength of its natural frequency of vibration.

In this context it is important that students should appreciate fully the difference between the symbol used to relate two or more canonical forms (↔) and that normally employed to indicate the presence of an *equilibrium* between species.

To summarise, organic dyes and pigments consist of an extended conjugated π-electron system to which are attached electron donor and acceptor groups (auxochromes). The absorption characteristics can be moved from the ultra-violet through the visible and even into the infra-red region of the electromagnetic spectrum by:

(a) Increasing the size of the conjugated system
(b) Adding donor or acceptor groups which further extend conjugation either directly (e.g. NO_2, CN) or by interaction of their non-bonding electrons with the π-system (e.g. NH_2, NR_2).

An approximate order of effectiveness of these donor and acceptor groups is given below:

Donors: NR_2 > NHR > NH_2 > OR > OH

Acceptors: NO_2 > CN > SO_2R > COOH.

Dyes may also contain groups which are introduced primarily to improve fastness properties, and almost all water-soluble dyes will have one or more sulphonic acid groups, usually in the form of their sodium salts (SO_3Na).

This brief survey of developments in what is a challenging area of chemistry has dealt only with qualitative treatments, though many of these remain in use today. Quantitative predictions of colour–constitution relationships are of increasing interest, now made more realisable by advances in molecular orbital theory and computer technology. Students interested in the latest developments in this field are referred to the comprehensive treatments previously published [1,2].

9.3 THE ORGANIC CHEMISTRY OF SYNTHETIC DYES
In principle, any given class of dyes must contain at least three members, covering the subtractive primaries yellow, red and blue. Mixtures of these allow the dyer to produce a range of colours, but for reasons of compatibility and fastness it is highly desirable to be able to produce some of these colours using homogeneous dyes rather than mixtures of yellow, red and blue. It is now possible for the dye chemist to produce homogeneous dyes of most colours with the important exception of a pure green, and this is achieved, by and large, with three chromogen systems:
(a) Arylazo
(b) Anthraquinone
(c) Copper phthalocyanine.

Azo compounds provide a wide range of hues but remain particularly strong in the yellow, orange and red areas; anthraquinone is the basis for a number of reds, bright blues, violets and blue-greens, while copper phthalocyanine gives predominantly blue and turquoise colours. Additionally a small number of dyes are derivatives of indigo and triarylmethanes, while others which have appeared more recently are based on new chromophoric systems such as benzodifuranone (VIII) and triphenodioxazine (IX).

The chemistry of the three main chromogenic systems is considered below, and special mention is made of the reactive and sulphur classes.

Azo dyes
This is by far the most important group. Azo dyes are characterised by their relative cheapness, high tinctorial strength (ε_{max} values are of the order $10^4 l/(mol\ cm)$ and nowadays fairly good coverage of the hue range, with yellows, reds and oranges particularly well represented. Examples are found in almost every dye class, e.g. direct, reactive and azoic types for cellulosic fibres; acid, metal-complex and reactive types for wool and nylon; disperse dyes for polyester and the cellulose acetates; and basic (cationic) dyes for acrylics. Most red, orange and yellow pigments are also azo compounds.

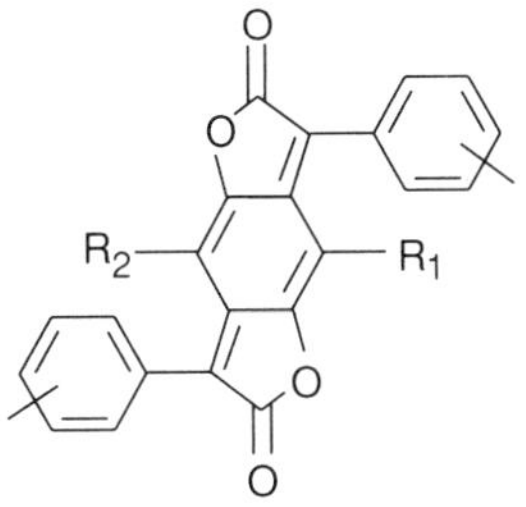

R_1, R_2 = H or halogen

VIII

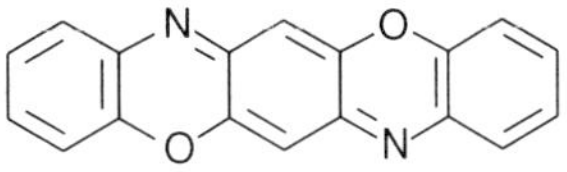

IX

Chemistry of azo dye synthesis

Azo dyes are synthesised by a two-stage process (diazotisation and coupling) which has remained almost unchanged since its discovery by Greiss in 1861.

Diazotisation involves the treatment of a primary aromatic amine ($ArNH_2$) with nitrous acid. In effect this is a nitrosation reaction and the exact nature of the nitrosating species varies with the reaction conditions used. Thus in the 'aqueous' process, a solution of sodium nitrite is added to a solution or suspension of the amine dissolved in hydrochloric acid, and it has been suggested that the nitrosating agent is N_2O_3 (Scheme 9.1).

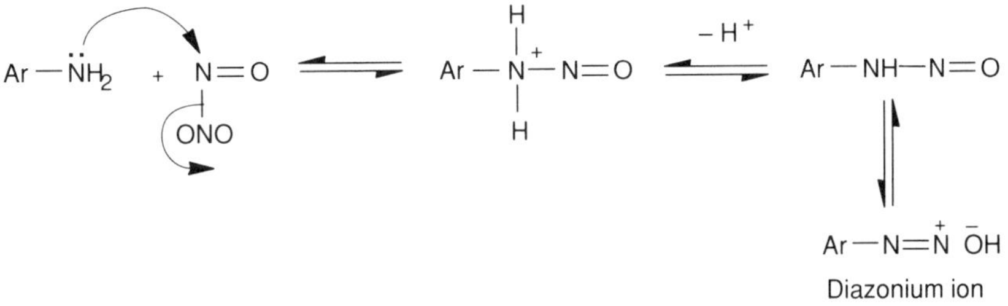

Diazonium ion

Scheme 9.1

Weakly basic amines (e.g. 2,4-dinitroaniline) require more rigorous conditions for diazotisation, and these are satisfied by the use of nitrosyl sulphuric acid ($NO^+HSO_4^-$) obtained by adding concentrated sulphuric acid to solid sodium nitrite, when the nitrosating species may be NO^+ or $HOSO_2ONO$. Aminophenols and aminonaphthols on the other hand require mild diazotising conditions due to the risk of the formation of quinones under the oxidising conditions.

Commercially important diazo components include chloroanilines, nitroanilines, 2-aminophenols, and aminonaphthols, the last two being used to build chelate structures into azo dyes for cotton and wool, and some heterocycles such as 2-aminothiophenes and 2-aminothiazoles which are now used in azo disperse dyes for polyester.

The diazonium ion formed above is a weak electrophile and will undergo an electrophilic substitution reaction with suitably activated coupling components. These coupling components are typically:

(a) Substituted naphthols – as in the synthesis of acid and mordant dyes for wool and direct and reactive dyes for cotton

(b) Substituted amines – as in the production of disperse dyes for polyester and basic dyes for acrylics

(c) Enolisable ketones – used specially for yellow acid dyes and yellow-orange pigments.

Thus with naphthols, Scheme 9.2 applies. Of the many naphthol derivatives the following may be mentioned as being of commercial importance as coupling components:
- 1-amino-2-naphthol-4-sulphonic acid for blue and black dyes for wool
- 6-amino-1-naphthol-3-sulphonic acid (J-acid) for reactive dyes for cotton
- 7-amino-1-naphthol-3-sulphonic acid (γ-acid) for a range of acid dyes for wool
- 1-amino-8-naphthol-3,6-disulphonic acid (H-acid) for acid dyes and direct and reactive cotton dyes.

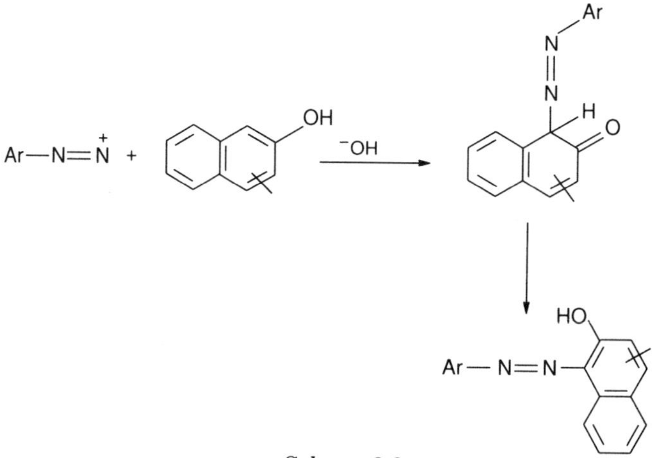

Scheme 9.2

Some dyes based on these coupling components are shown below (X–XII). Structure XII also illustrates the importance of 2-aminophenols as diazo components in chelate structures.

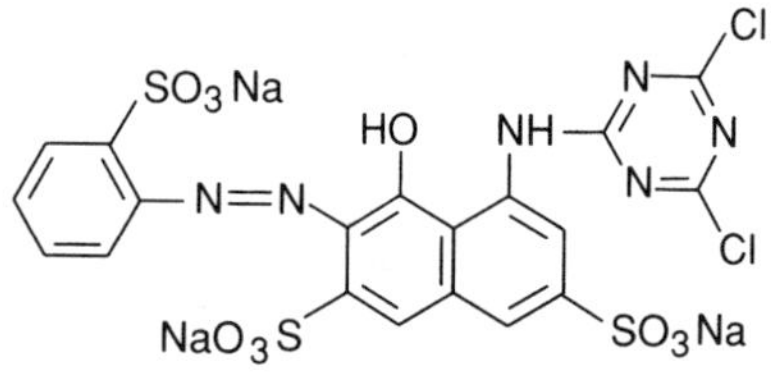

X, C.I. Reactive Red 1

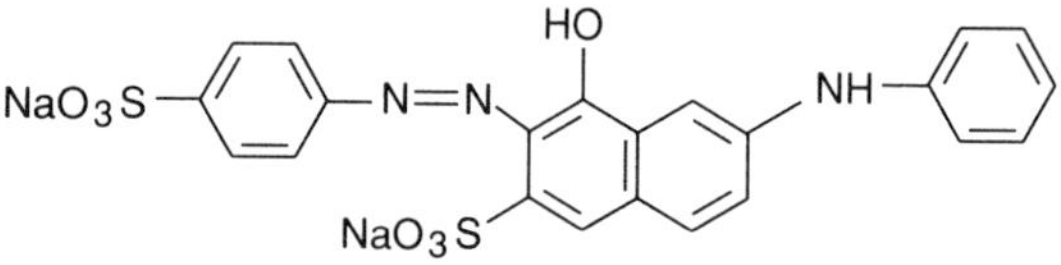

XI, C.I. Acid Brown 86

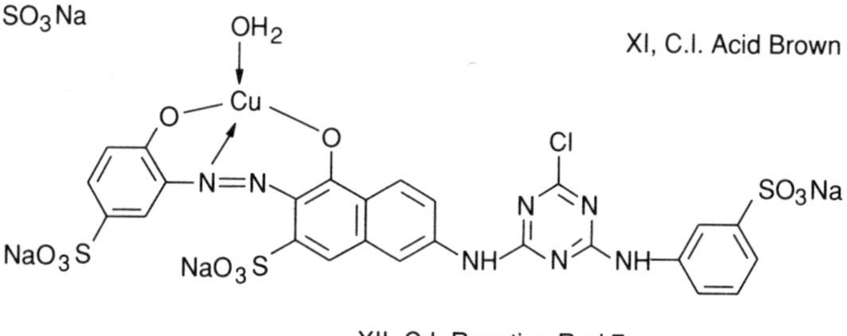

XII, C.I. Reactive Red 7

Monoazo dyes have little affinity for cellulose but the discovery that arylamides of 3-hydroxy-2-naphthoic acid did have moderate affinity led to the azoic dyeing process whereby insoluble monoazo colorants were synthesised *in situ*. Impregnation of cotton with alkaline solutions of these arylamides, followed by treatment in solutions of diazotised anilines, gave a range of 'azoic dyes'. These are predominantly red (XIII) and bordeaux shades, with important yellow and black combinations, all characterised by good all-round fastness properties.

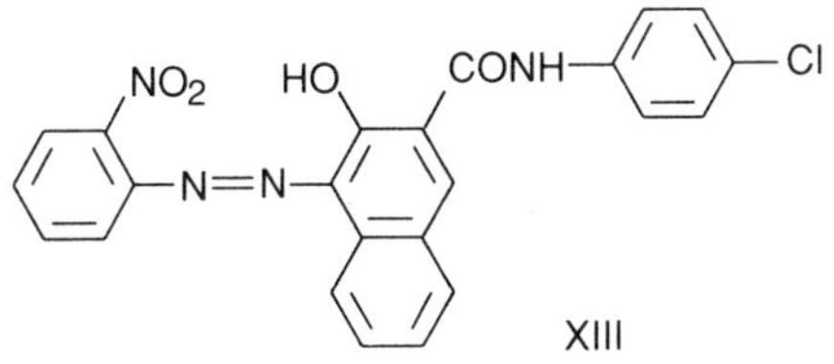

XIII

The coupling reaction between diazonium ions and amines takes place in a similar way but under slightly acidic conditions. This sequence is particularly important in the manufacture of aminoazobenzene disperse dyes for polyester. Typically the diazo component contains electron-withdrawing groups (NO_2, CN, Cl) and the amine coupling component electron donors (NR_2, OCH_3, $NHCOCH_3$), and increasing degrees of substitution extends the colour range from orange through red to blue (XIV–XVI).

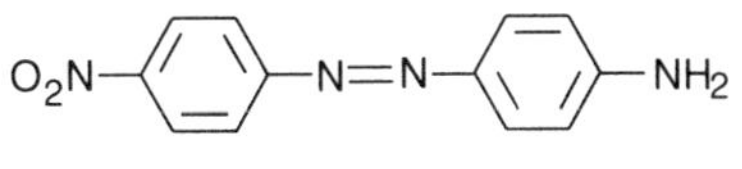

XIV, C.I. Disperse Orange 1

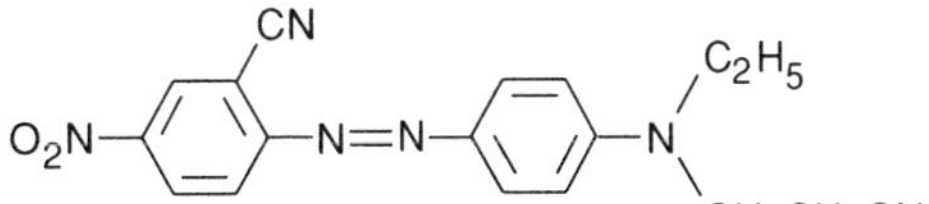

XV, C.I. Disperse Red 72

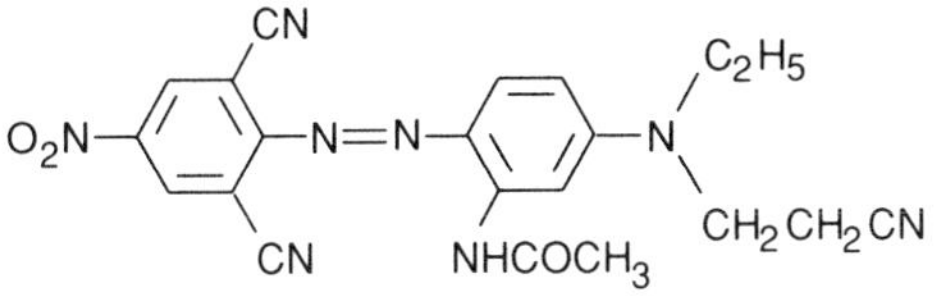

XVI, Blue disperse dye

The use of heterocyclic diazo components has extended the colour range of these dyes to cover the blue and blue-green areas. Dye XVII is a blue disperse dye prepared from the diazo component 2-amino-3,5-dinitrothiophene.

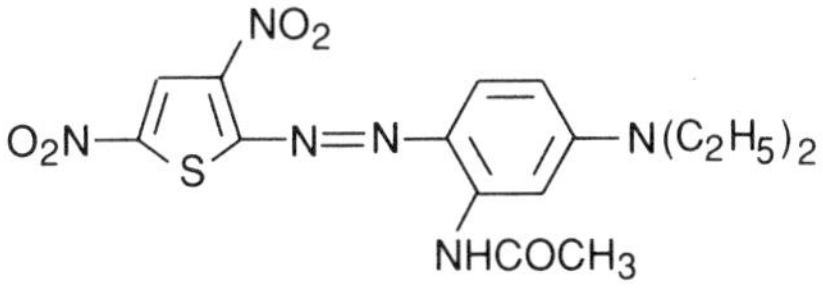

XVII

Similar couplings of diazotised nitro- and chloro-anilines with quaternised dialkylanilines give yellow, orange and red-brown pendant azo dyes for acrylic fibres. The positive charge of the quaternary nitrogen allows dyes such as XVIII to bind to acidic sites in the fibre.

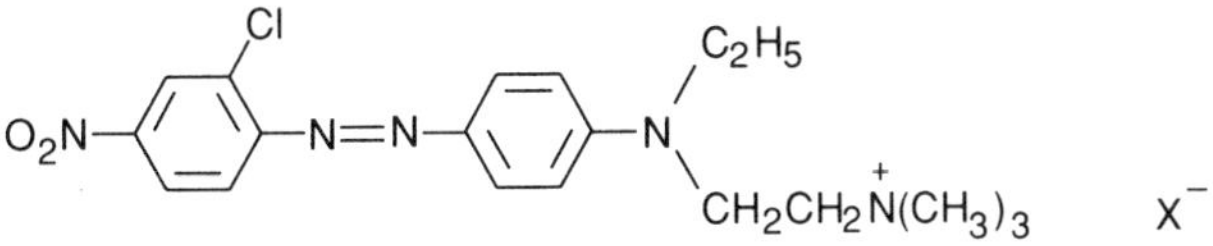

XVIII

The most important of the enolisable ketones used as coupling components are those based on the pyrazolone heterocyclic system (XIX), and on acetoacetarylamides (XX). Both types enolise readily and coupling takes place on the carbon adjacent to the oxygen function in structure XIX and that between the two oxygen functions in structure XX.

XIX   XX

The colorants derived from these coupling components are restricted to the bright yellow-orange area and are typified by C.I. Acid Yellow 17 (XXI), a bright acid dye with high light fastness on wool and nylon, and C.I. Pigment Yellow 1 (XXII). Pyrazolone coupling components are also used to produce, for example, yellow reactive dyes for cotton. Structure XXII has been written in the hydrazone rather than the more conventional azo form since the former is stabilised by two intramolecularly hydrogen-bonded rings. Indeed most azo dyes which contain suitably placed hydroxyls (e.g. *ortho* to the azo group) exist as the hydrazone tautomeric form.

XXI   XXII

Substantivity for cellulose requires longer molecular structures than those provided by monoazo dyes, and this has been achieved in the direct dyes by introducing second and even third (or more) azo groups into the dye structure. Although the range of direct dyes is now less extensive than it was before the banning of the carcinogenic diamine benzidine, this class still plays an important role in the coloration of cellulosic textiles as well as that of paper. The wet fastness of the dyes on cotton is generally low. Typically (e.g. dye XXIII) these polyazo dyes are long linear or planar molecules containing two or more sulphonic acid groups to confer water solubility. The additional azo group(s) can be introduced in a number of ways, e.g. by the use of coupling components containing suitably placed amino groups which can then be diazotised.

XXIII

Anthraquinonoid dyes

Dyes based on anthraquinone are found among vat and reactive classes for cellulosics, acid and reactive types for wool and nylon, disperse dyes for polyester and cellulose acetate fibres and basic (cationic) dyes for acrylic fibres. With the exception of vat dyes with their polynuclear systems, anthraquinonoid dyes are still pre-eminent in the bright blue to bright red range and this, coupled with high intrinsic light fastness, has made them second only to the azo dyes in commercial importance. They are, however, tinctorially weaker (ε_{max} is about half that of the azo group) and more expensive than azo dyes.

Chemistry of anthraquinonoid dyes

Unlike the synthesis of azo compounds the anthraquinone chromogen must first be assembled and substituent groups attached at a later stage. Since anthraquinone is a deactivated ring system due to the electron-withdrawing carbonyl groups, normal aromatic electrophilic substitution is not easy in many cases, and impossible in others. Thus the only two electrophilic substitution reactions used extensively are nitration and sulphonation, direct halogenation not being possible. Anthraquinone-2-sulphonic acid is the favoured product of a sulphonation reaction, though it is the 1-isomer that is often required, since this will undergo nucleophilic substitition to give 1-substituted aminoanthraquinones. The attachment of the sulphonate group into the 1-position requires the use of a mercury(II) catalyst. Thus the important auxochromes NH_2 and OH are introduced via nucleophilic substitution, and not, as might be expected in the former case, by reduction of a nitro group. Boric acid is often used as a catalyst in these reactions, complexing between the carbonyl group(s) and suitable substituents in the 1- (and 4-) positions. The importance of electron donors in these positions on the resulting colour is shown below (structure XXIV), and all anthraquinonoid dyes are substituted in this way. This allows a transfer of charge between donor groups and the carbonyl acceptors, a feature already noted in structure II(f) and also found in the aminoazobeneze disperse dyes XIV–XVI. Hydrogen-carrying substituents in the 1- and/or 4-positions also form intramolecular hydrogen bonds with carbonyl oxygens, a feature which is thought to contribute to the good light fastness of anthraquinonoid dyes.

XXIV

Two intermediates long used in anthraquinonoid dye chemistry are quinizarin (XXV) and 'bromamine acid' (XXVI).

XXV

XXVI

From compound XXV a range of early 1,4-diamino-substituted blue disperse dyes have been prepared while compound XXVI is an important intermediate in the production of bright blue acid dyes for wool and nylon. These products are typified by dyes XXIV (R_1 = R_2 = NHCH$_3$) and XXVII respectively.

Early basic (cationic) blue dyes of the pendant type for acrylics (dye XXVIII) were also 1,4-diaminoanthraquinone derivatives.

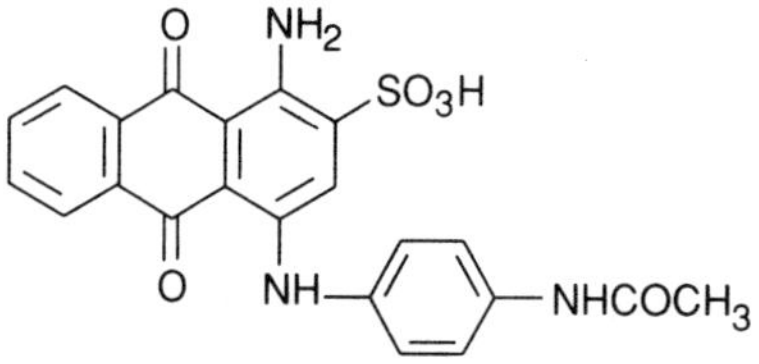

XXVII, C.I. Acid Blue 40

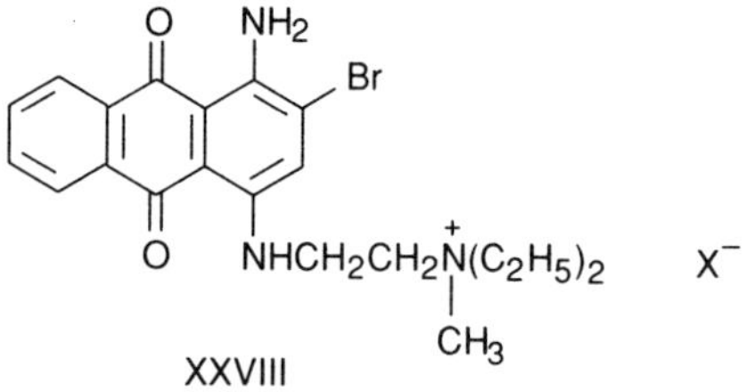

XXVIII

More recent developments in anthraquinone dye chemistry have centred on 1-amino-4-hydroxy-2-oxy-substituted disperse dyes which form an important group of bright reds for polyester, of which dye XXIX is an example.

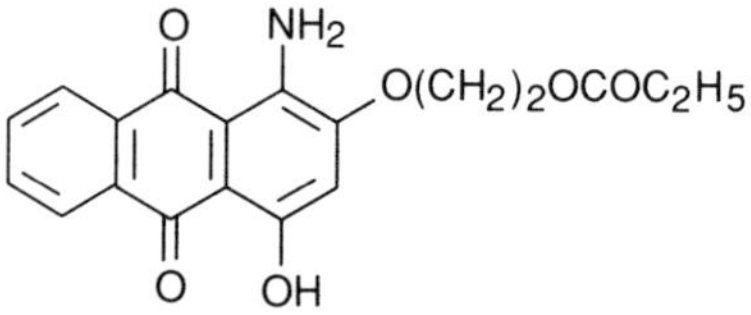

XXIX

Due to the inherent weaknesses of anthraquinonoid dyes (low tinctorial strength, high cost and use of mercury catalysts), much research effort has been expended by dyestuff manufacturers to replace them. That this has not been successful testifies to the excellence of the technical properties of anthraquinonoid dyes, and it seems likely that the group will remain an important one for some time. Students wishing to follow some of the attempts to replace anthraquinonoid reactive and disperse dyes with other types are referred to published reviews [3,4].

Anthraquinone will continue to be important for the manufacture of vat dyes as long as this dye class is used for fast dyeings on cellulosic fibres. Anthraquinonoid vat dyes based on polycyclic systems such as indanthrone (XXX), flavanthrone (XXXI) and pyranthrone (XXXII) give a range of yellow, orange, brown, blue and green shades.

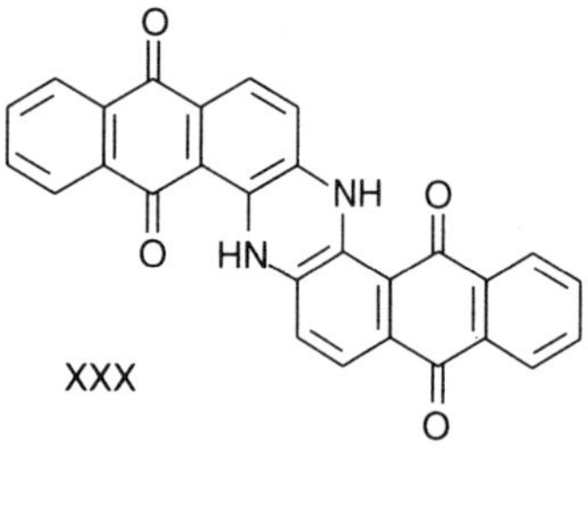

XXX

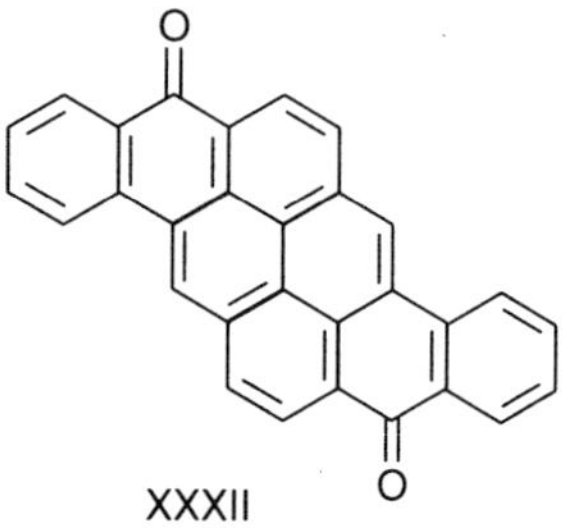

XXXII

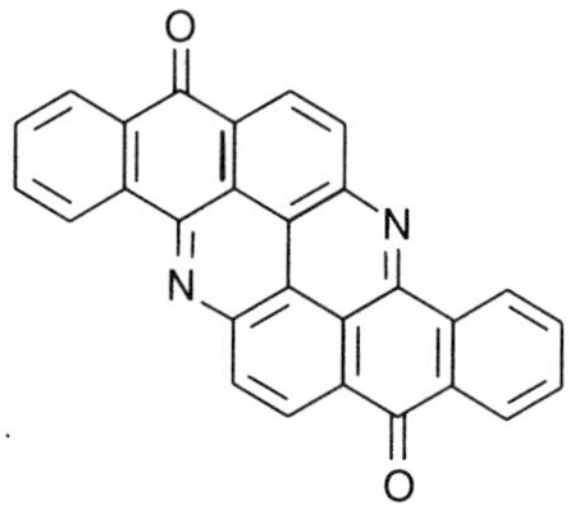

XXXI

Dyes based on copper phthalocyanine

Copper phthalocyanine (XXXIII) is an outstanding blue pigment which crystallises in two commercially important forms, the stable β (greener) form and the metastable α (redder) form. Much research has been devoted to exploiting the phthalocyanine nucleus as a dye owing to its outstanding brightness and light fastness. Consequently phthalocyanine-based structures have appeared as direct, ingrain and reactive dyes for cotton, and acid dyes for wool.

XXXIII

Direct sulphonation of compound XXXIII gives a disulphonated product (C.I. Direct Blue 86) which, as a direct dye, retains the brightness of the parent compound but has poor wet fastness properties. In C.I. Acid Blue 249, a tetrasulphonated product, the sulphonic acid groups are introduced at the phthalocyanine synthesis stage by using 4-sulpho phthalic acid (XXXIV) as a precursor. This product has lower affinity for cellulose than has the disulphonate and has found some use as an acid dye. Some other water-soluble dyes based on copper phthalocyanine have subsequently been introduced, of the general type XXXV.

XXXIV

$m = 4, \; n = 0$
$m = 2, \; n = 2$

XXXV

The Alcian (ICI) range of dyes gave bright blue and blue-green shades on cellulose, their fastness depending on the presence of a temporary solubilising quaternary group which at a later stage in the dyeing cycle was removed by treatment with alkali. These dyes were typified by structures such as XXXVI, but are no longer marketed.

XXXVI

The most ingenious attempt to exploit the blue pigment as a dye was the *in situ* synthesis that formed the basis of the Phthalogen dyes (BAY). This involved the use of reactive isoindolenine precursors, the first of which was marketed as Phthalogen Brilliant Blue IF3G (XXXVII). After impregnation, heating to 140°C, or aqueous reduction with alkaline dithionite, resulted in the formation of the phthalocyanine pigment *in situ*. Bright fast dyeings of brilliant blue to blue-green shades were obtained on cellulose.

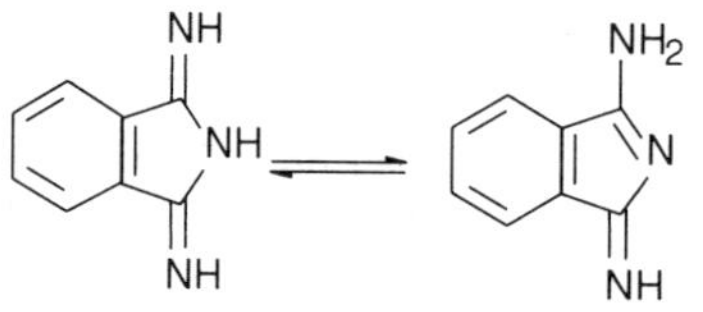

XXXVII

Turquoise dyes in the reactive dye ranges are based on the copper phthalocyanine chromophore and are typified by dyes **XXXVIII** and **XXXIX**.

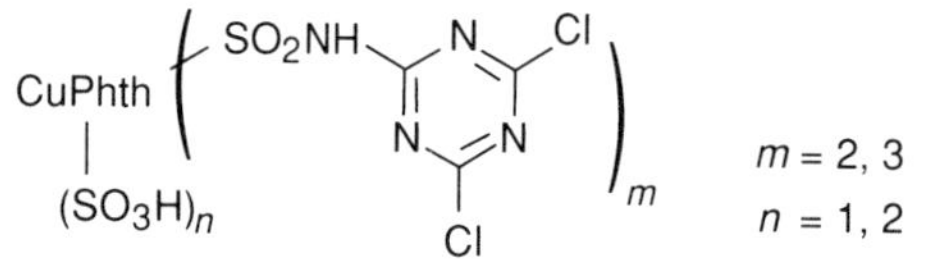

XXXVIII

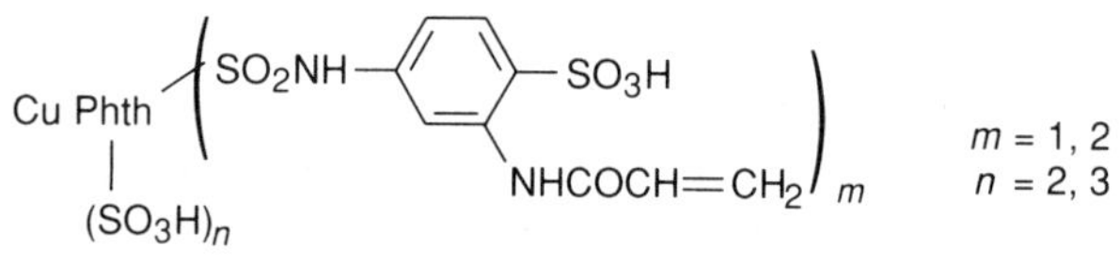

XXXIX

Reactive dyes

This group constitutes a rather special case in that developments in its chemistry have centred on the reactive nucleus rather than on the chromogen system. The first commercial fibre-reactive dyes were introduced for the dyeing of cotton by continuous methods, and as such required to have a low substantivity for the fibre. This was conveniently achieved by using existing acid dye chromogens, characterised by brightness of shade, and linking these to a moeity which under suitable conditions would react chemically with the fibre. The chromogens used then, and subsequently, cover the types already mentioned, i.e. yellow, red and orange dyes were azo compounds, bright blues were anthraquinone derivatives while the turquoise range was covered by copper phthalocyanine derivatives. Darker shades, browns, greys, navies and blacks, were obtained using 1:2 chromium and 1:1 copper complexes of o,o'-dihydroxyazo dyes.

The ability of cellulose to react chemically with suitable dyes depends on the fact that, under alkaline conditions, its hydroxyl groups are partially ionised. The cellulosate anion Cell–O⁻ is a nucleophile which can take part in the following reactions:
(a) Nucleophilic substitution reactions with certain aromatic heterocycles, as typified by the original Procion (ICI) dyes introduced in 1956
(b) Nucleophilic addition at activated ethylenic carbons – a form of the Michael reaction, e.g. the Remazol (HOE) dyes.

The Procion dyes were based on the cyanuric chloride (2,4,6-trichloro-1,3,5-triazine) heterocycle (XL) and the original red dye (X) is a typical reactive dye consisting of a monoazo acid dye structure (orthanilic acid → H-acid) linked to the reactive grouping through an imino bridging group.

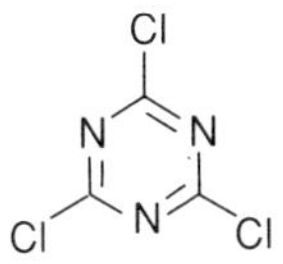

XL

Reaction with ionised cellulose proceeds by attack at the electron-deficient carbons of the heterocyclic ring (Scheme 9.3).

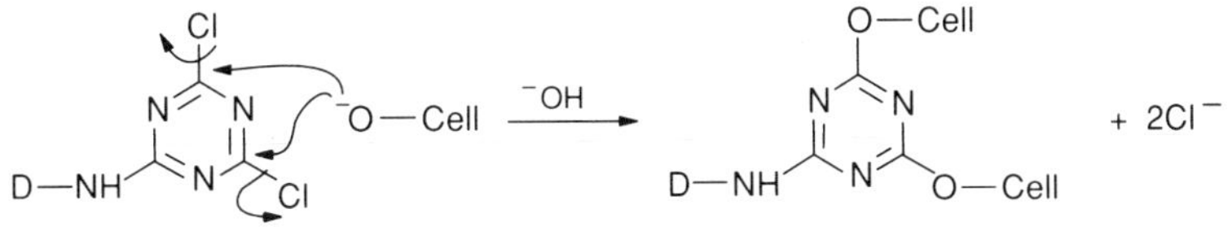

Scheme 9.3

The reactive system used by Hoechst in the Remazol range was quite different in character. The reactive moiety here is the vinylsulphone ($-SO_2CH=CH_2$) group, generated *in situ* from the sulphate esters of hydroxyethylsulphonyl precursors (XLI).

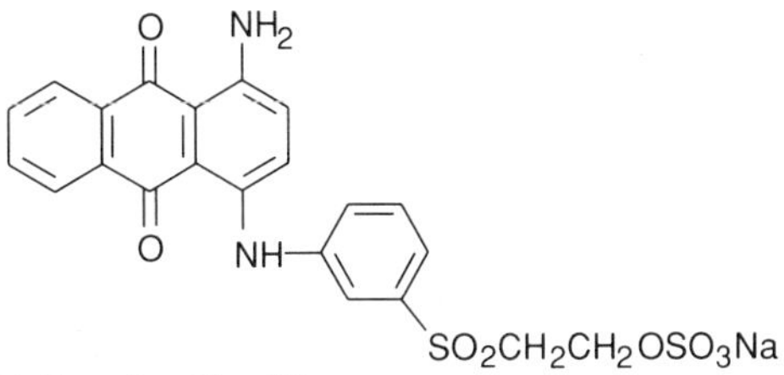

XLI, C.I. Reactive Blue 19

The electron-deficient sulphur atom activates the ethylenic carbon atom towards nucleophilic addition as in the Michael reaction (Scheme 9.4).

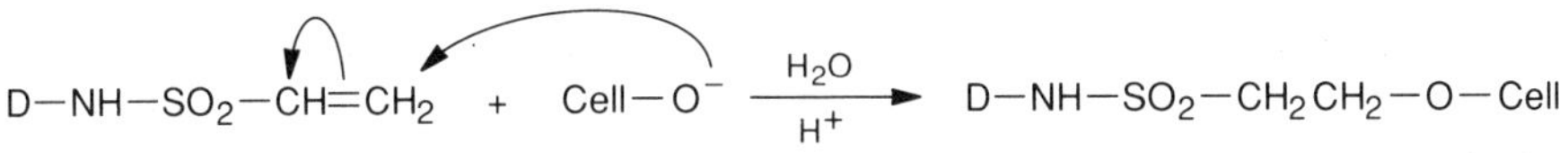

Scheme 9.4

Amino and other groups in wool are potential nucleophiles, and reactive dyes have subsequently been developed which react with wool by this type of nucleophilic addition. Thus the Lanasol (CGY) range uses the α-bromoacrylamido ($-NHCOC(Br)=CH_2$) reactive grouping in which the ethylenic linkage is activated by the electron-withdrawing bromine as well as the adjacent carbonyl group.

Research over the last 30 years has been directed towards improving the efficiency of the dye–fibre reaction (as well as other technical properties) by introducing changes in the reactive groupings in dyes for cotton. Replacement of one of the halogens in compound XL by NH_2, NHAlk, NHAr or OCH_3 allows the degree of reactivity to be controlled (Procion H (ICI), Cibacron and Cibacron Pront (CGY) ranges), while the use of a diazine pyrimidine heterocycle (XLII) in the Drimarene (S) ranges gave dyes of lower reactivity but improved aqueous solubility. The Levafix range (BAY) uses 2,3-dichloroquinoxaline (XLIII) as the reactive nucleus. The chlorine atoms are relatively unreactive, but the introduction of an acid chloride group in the 6-position, through which chromogens were linked, gives reactive dyes that react with cellulose at the carbon at the 2-position.

Fluorine has been claimed to be about a hundred times more efficient than chlorine as a leaving group and fluorinated heterocycles such as 5-chloro-2,4,6-trifluoropyrimidine (XLIV) have been used in the Verofix (BAY) range for wool, in which the chromogen is linked through the fluorine at C_4 and the fibre reaction takes place at C_2 and C_6. The Cibacron F (CGY) range for cellulosic fibres uses a monofluorotriazine ring system.

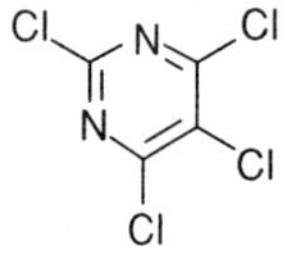

XLII 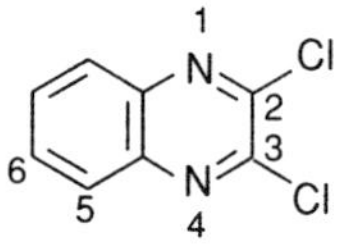   XLIII 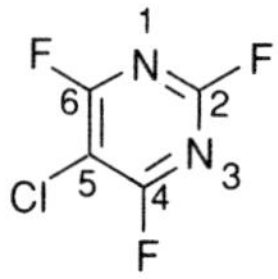   XLIV

The use of small acid dye chromogens in reactive dyes for brightness of shade meant that these dyes had low substantivity for cellulose, and large amounts of salt were required if they were used for batch dyeing. In an attempt to overcome this, dyes with two reactive groups per molecule were introduced (Procion H-E, (ICI)) to give a higher degree of fibre fixation (e.g. dye XLV).

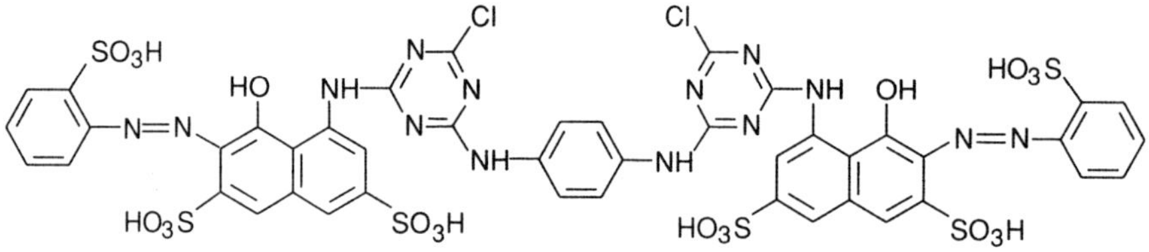

XLV, C.I. Reactive Red 120

The same approach has been adopted in ranges of dyes specifically designed for printing, in which high degrees of fixation and easy removal of unfixed dye are desirable. More recently the idea has been further extended with the appearance of bifunctional dyes containing two different (e.g. chlorotriazinyl and vinylsulphone) reactive systems.

One of the textile growth areas in recent years has been that of polyester/cellulosic blends, and this resulted in the development of a reactive dye system (Procion T, ICI) which could be applied under the same conditions as, and simultaneously with, disperse dyes. The system employed a phosphonic acid group, and in the presence of a catalyst (cyanamide) reaction with cellulose proceeded according to Scheme 9.5. Dye XLVI was an example of a yellow dye from this range, which has recently been withdrawn.

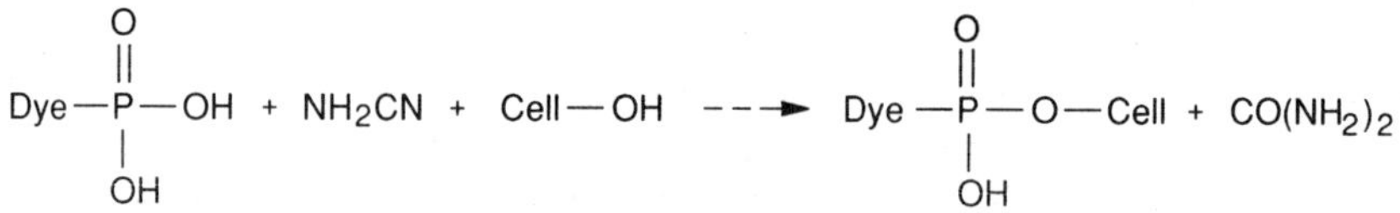

Scheme 9.5

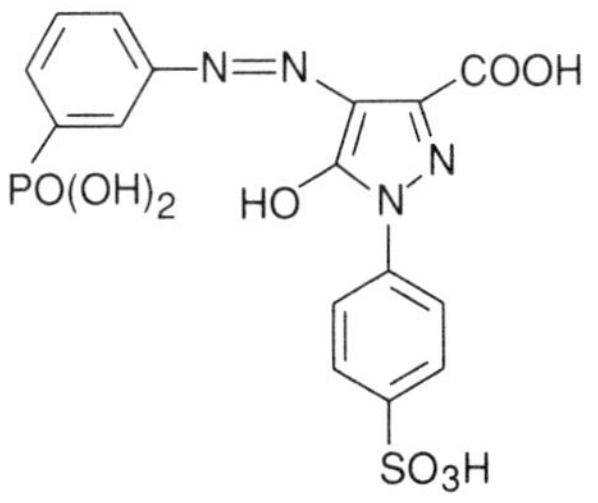

XLVI

Much effort has thus gone into the development of new reactive dyes since their appearance in 1956. Though most of this work has centred on the reactive system itself, there is now increasingly an interest in producing novel chromogens, particularly lower cost ones. Two developments in this area may be mentioned. The greenish-yellow pyridone dye XLVII is tinctorially about half as strong again as similar dyes of the azo–pyrazolone type.

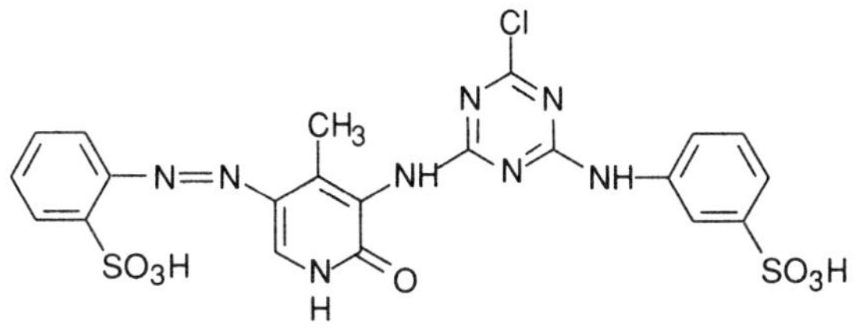

XLVII

Recently reactive dyes based on the triphenodioxazine chromogen (IX) have appeared as replacements for blue dyes based on anthraquinone. Structure IX has been linked to a number of reactive systems, including mono- and di-chlorotriazinyl, fluorotriazinyl, and phosphonic acid, to give blue reactive dyes which are tinctorially about four times as strong as their anthraquinone counterparts. It seems likely that future research in the field of reactive (and other) dyes will be directed towards the discovery of new heterocyclic chromogens to cover other areas of the colour gamut.

Sulphur dyes

Mention must be made of this class for two reasons. Firstly sulphur dyes, along with directs, continue to dominate the dyeing of cellulosic fibres in terms of dyestuff consumption, and secondly no precise formulae can be assigned to them, chemical considerations being restricted to intermediates and details of manufacture.

Various types of compound, mainly aromatic, when heated with sulphur or alkali polysulphides (thionation) give sulphur dyes. Thus nitrophenols, substituted diphenyl amines, aminonaphthalenes, indophenols (e.g. compound XLVIII), and polycyclics such as decacyclene (XLIX) and perylene (L) have all been thionated to give commercial products. Treatment of 2,4-dinitrophenol with a polysulphide solution results in reduction to the diaminophenol and then thionation to give sulphur black, one of the most widely used of all dyestuffs.

XLVIII

XLIX

L

The thionation process is thought to result in the formation of disulphide linkages attached to the aromatic ring and these are converted in an alkaline sodium sulphide dyebath to soluble –S⁻Na⁺ groups with substantivity for cotton. On air oxidation, insoluble disulphides are re-formed *in situ*. There is a wide range of dullish yellow, orange, khaki, brown, blue and even red shades available, and chromogenic systems such as thiazole (LI) and phenothiazinone (LII) have been identified as contributing to the colour of these dyes.

LI   LII

Some blue and green sulphur dyes are made from copper phthalocyanine by a modification of the normal thionation process involving chlorsulphonation of the phthalocyanine, subsequent reduction being effected by the addition of zinc dust.

It has only been possible in this short section to touch briefly on what is a complex but fascinating area of organic chemistry, and those wishing to extend their knowledge are referred to the bibliography at the end of the chapter.

9.4 THE ORGANIC CHEMISTRY OF NATURAL COLOURING MATTERS

Many compounds have been extracted from plant and animal sources and used in the coloration of textiles prior to and, in some cases, well beyond the introduction of synthetic dyestuffs. Today there remain numerous examples of multi-coloured textiles which are a testament to the artistic and technical skills of dyers down through the ages, and the chemistry of some of the more important natural colouring matters used in these times is briefly considered below.

Yellows

This group is numerically more important than reds, blues and other hues, though the colorants are generally less fast (particularly with respect to light) than other groups. Chemically the yellows can be subdivided into two distinct chemical groups:
(a) Flavonoids and related compounds
(b) Polyenes.

The general flavonoid chromogen (LIII) contains hydroxyl groups, usually at the 3-, 5-, 7-, 3'- and 4'-positions. Compounds with a hydrogen at the 3-position (R_1 = H) are flavonones while the 3-hydroxy derivatives (R_1 = OH) are called flavonols. Some of the best known examples of this class are:

– Persian berries   ($R_1 = R_2 = R_4 = R_5 = OH$; $R_3 = OCH_3$)
– Quercitin   ($R_1 = R_2 = R_3 = R_4 = R_5 = OH$)
– Weld   ($R_1 = H$; $R_2 = R_3 = R_4 = R_5 = OH$).

LIII

Weld, a flavonone, has superior light fastness to the flavonols. Two other natural dyes have related structures. The petals of the plant dyer's thistle contain safflower yellow (the constitution of which is unknown) and carthamin (LIV), C.I. Natural Red 26, while maclurin (LV) is a substituted benzophenone and is a minor consituent of old fustic a brownish-yellow dye.

LIV   LV

These and similar compounds gave brilliant yellow to yellow-brown shades on wool and silk (and sometimes cotton) when applied with aluminium or tin mordants. The intensity of the colour is greatest in these compounds having adjacent hydroxyls (e.g. R_4 and R_5 in compound LIII). Those lacking this structural feature were not employed as dyestuffs.

Some of the chemically related anthocyanins, e.g. compound LVI, are now used as natural colorants in soft drinks. They occur widely in flowers, fruits and berries.

The less important polyene group of yellows includes saffron (LVII) and the closely related annatto. Saffron has recently been used as a replacement for the yellow azo food colour tartrazine (C.I. Food Yellow 4), while annatto is also used now as a food colorant in confectionery and cheese.

LVI

LVII

Reds

The important red natural colouring matters are hydroxyanthraquinone derivatives (LVIII) and include

- Madder   ($R_1 = R_2 = OH$; $R_3 = R_4 = R_5 = R_6 = R_7 = H$)
- Kermes   ($R_1 = R_3 = R_4 = R_6 = OH$; $R_2 = COCH_3$; $R_5 = COOH$; $R_7 = CH_3$)
- Purpurin ($R_1 = R_2 = R_4 = OH$; $R_3 = R_5 = R_6 = R_7 = H$).

The closely related cochineal (LIX) has a sugar group attached at the 2-position.

LVIII

LIX

In the main components of lac, another red dye of antiquity, the ring system at the 2-position is aromatic. All these anthraquinone reds were applied on mordants of aluminium or tin, mainly on wool and silk, though latterly other metals such as chromium were also used, and this type of colorant gave bright shades of outstanding (at the time) fastness. The most famous example was probably Turkey red, a brilliant red calcium and aluminium complex of madder widely used in printed cotton goods until replaced by azoic reds.

Blues and purples

The main naturally occuring blue dye was undoubtedly indigotin (LX, $R_1 = R_2 = H$), or indigo as it is more widely known. Its dibromo derivative, Tyrian purple (LX, $R_1 = R_2 = Br$) was also an important, if rare, dye in ancient times.

The popularity of denim jeans in recent times led to a renewed interest in the manufacture of synthetic indigo. The product obtained by sulphonating indigo gives a water-soluble blue acid dye, brighter than the parent insoluble compound, but showing poor wet and light fastness.

A number of beautiful, but fugitive, purple and mauve colouring matters were produced by the action of nitrogen donors (ammonia or stale urine) on certain lichens. These were called variously orchil, cudbear, orcein and archil, and structure LXI has been proposed as the chromogenic system.

LX

LXI

$R_1 = H,$

$R_2 = O, NH$

$R_3 = OH, NH_2$

Black

The most important naturally occurring black dyestuff was logwood or Campeachy wood. The colouring matter is haematoxylin or more properly its oxidation product haematin (LXII).

LXII

Logwood was used for dyeing blacks on wool, silk and cotton (and more recently nylon) as well as for other colours such as blue, green and brown. The colour obtained depends on the mordant, chromium and iron giving black. The oldest of the logwood blacks, established before the introduction of chromium as a mordant, was the 'copperas black', produced on wool with a mordant of iron and copper.

In concluding this short section on natural dyes, it must be pointed out that many of these consist of mixtures of chemically related compounds, and the structures given for the flavonoid yellows and the anthraquinonoid reds are those for the major components in such mixtures.

9.5 THE CHEMICAL AND PHYSICAL STRUCTURE OF TEXTILE FIBRES

Textile fibres are composed of molecules that are very long and flexible, as are the fibres themselves. All such fibrous molecules can be described as polymeric in nature, consisting essentially of many hundreds or even thousands of identical chemical repeat units joined end-to-end to form polymer chains, but also held together by a variety of inter-chain forces and bonds as discussed below and in section 10.1. The repeat units of the more important fibrous molecules are given in Figure 9.1.

Although chemical structure has a marked effect on dyeing properties, the packing of the molecular chains and their organisation, i.e. the microphysical state of the fibre, influence the dyeability by controlling the access of water and dye molecules into the internal regions of the fibre structure.

The chain-packing characteristics of the linear polymeric molecules of textile fibres have been explained in terms of models in which the molecular chains are arranged in different degrees of order varying from the completely disordered or amorphous condition to the partially oriented crystalline condition.

Both orientation and crystallinity influence the kinetics and equilibrium uptake of water and dye molecules by fibres. With a natural fibre the molecular alignment is an inherent characteristic of that fibre determined by its growth behaviour. Thus the cellulosic fibre jute, which comes from a plant stem, has a higher degree of orientation than cotton fibres, which are seed hairs designed to help seed dispersal rather than give plant support. However, even within the cotton fibre the outer layers (the primary cellulose layers) are more highly ordered and more resistant to water penetration (and swelling)

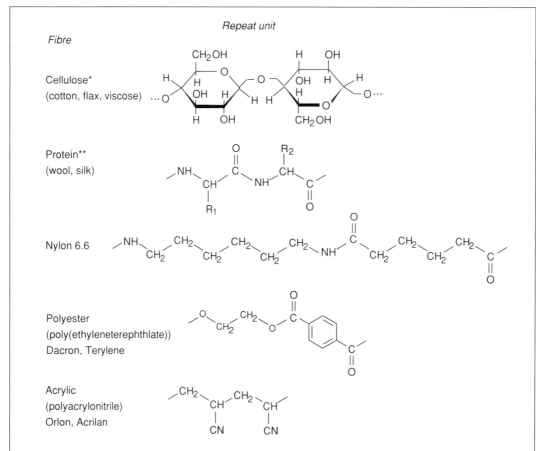

*   In cellulose triacetate fibres the three hydroxyl groups in each glucose ring are acetylated to –OCOCH$_3$ ester groups, whilst with ordinary (secondary) cellulose acetate a small proportion of the hydroxyl groups (about 0.7 per glucose unit) is left unacetylated. The esterification of the hydroxyl groups considerably modifies the interchain bonding (hydrogen bonding, cf. section 10.1, is significantly reduced) and this has a marked effect on thermal behaviour, solvent solubility, moisture uptake and the nature of the dyes applicable (disperse dyes were first designed for application to the hydrophobic secondary cellulose acetate, cf. Chapter 9).

**   In protein fibres R$_1$ and R$_2$ represent different amino acid residues, of which in excess of 20 have been found in wool fibres; of these a number terminate in amino (NH$_2$) or carboxyl (COOH) groups which are of importance because of their influence in dyeing (cf. section 10.1). An important difference between wool and silk is the presence in the former of the cystine or disulphide (–CH$_2$–S–S–CH$_2$) cross-linking amino acid residue. This causes wool to be insoluble in any solvent without degradation, but is also responsible for many of the desirable physical properties of wool such as its reversible extensibility and its crease-resist behaviour.

Figure 9.1 – Repeat units of fibres

than are the core or secondary cellulose layers. With synthetic fibres the crystallinity can be controlled by both chemical structural variations and/or by the rate of cooling after polymerisation, whilst the degree of orientation is controlled both at the initial extrusion stage and, more importantly, at the subsequent drawing stage.

One particular property that is fundamental to the behaviour of polymer molecules under thermal stress is the mobility of the molecular chains as characterised by their second-order or glass transition temperature, T_g. This temperature is defined as that at which changes occur in the properties of the non-crystalline regions. On the molecular level it is believed to be the temperature at which segments of the molecular chains are free to rotate, and physically the polymer changes from a glass-like state, at temperatures below T_g to one which is more flexible and rubber-like at temperatures above T_g. The changes in physical properties that occur at and above the T_g of a particular fibre can significantly affect the dyeability of that fibre, by allowing the formation of new or changing voids within the polymer and thus influencing the diffusion of water and dye molecules.

The value of T_g can be changed by small variations in chemical structure, by copolymerisation with a small proportion of suitable monomeric material (designed either to increase or decrease chain rigidity as required), or by the presence of certain dyebath additives, e.g. carriers in the dyeing of polyesters (section 8.6). The T_g can also be influenced by the degree of crystallinity achieved, e.g. with poly(ethylene terephthalate) the value of T_g increases continuously from 81 to 122°C as the crystallinity increases from zero to 65%. Over the last 30 years or so the fibre manufacturer has been able to engineer the polymerisation, extrusion and fibre-forming processes to produce synthetic fibres with a wide-range of chemical, physical and dyeing properties.

The influences of fibre structure on dyeing properties is an extensive subject and has been dealt with in more detail elsewhere [5].

REFERENCES

1. J Griffiths, Rev. Prog. Coloration, **14** (1984) 21.
2. J Griffiths, 'Colour and constitution of organic molecules' (London: Academic Press, 1976).
3. A H M Renfrew, Rev. Prog. Coloration, **15** (1985) 15.
4. O Annen et al, Rev. Prog. Coloration, **17** (1987) 72.
5. W C Ingamells in 'The theory of coloration of textiles', Ed. A Johnson (Bradford: SDC, 1989).

BIBLIOGRAPHY

1. 'The chemistry of synthetic dyes', Vols. 1–8, Ed. K Venkataraman (New York: Academic Press).
2. P F Gordon and P Gregory, 'Organic chemistry in colour' (New York: Springer-Verlag, 1983).
3. G Hallas in 'Developments in the chemistry and technology of organic dyes', Critical reports on applied chemistry, Vol. 7, Ed. J Griffiths (Oxford: Blackwell Scientific Publications, 1984) 31.
4. H Zollinger 'Colour chemistry' (Weinheim: VCH, 1987).
5. R L M Allen, 'Colour chemistry' (London: Nelson, 1971).
6. C V Stead, Rev. Prog. Coloration, **1** (1969) 23 (azo dyes – acid, direct, metal-complex, reactive, disperse, basic).
7. C V Stead, Rev. Prog. Coloration, **6** (1975) 1 (direct and acid dyes).
8. U Baumgarte, Rev. Prog. Coloration, **5** (1974) 17 (vat dyes).
9. J F Dawson, Rev. Prog. Coloration, **3** (1972) 18; **9** (1978) 25; **14** (1984) 90; R K Fourness Rev. Prog. Coloration, **10** (1979) 61 (disperse dyes).
10. F Beffa and E Steiner, Rev. Prog. Coloration, **4** (1973) 60 (metal-containing dyes).
11. U Mayer and E Seipmann, Rev. Prog. Coloration, **5** (1974) 65; R Raue, Rev. Prog. Coloration, **14** (1984) 187 (cationic (basic) dyes).
12. R R Davies, Rev. Prog. Coloration, **3** (1972) 73; P Rosenthal, Rev. Prog. Coloration, **7** (1976) 23; F R Alsberg, Rev. Prog. Coloration, **12** (1982) 66; I D Rattee, Rev. Prog. Coloration, **14** (1984) 50 (reactive dyes).
13. W E Wood, Rev. Prog. Coloration, **7** (1976) 80 (sulphur dyes).

10 THEORETICAL ASPECTS OF DYEING

For well over a hundred years scientists and dyestuff chemists have been engaged in the synthesis of organic dyes, and from the early years of the century a corresponding effort has gone into the study of the chemical and physical properties of fibres. During much of that time the dyer, who had successfully to apply the one to the other, achieved his aim using traditional, empirical methods and it was not until the 1950s that Vickerstaff in his well known book [1] made an attempt to examine the dyeing process in terms of physico-chemical principles. While the transfer of dye from a dyebath to a fibre appears deceptively simple, the application of the thermodynamic and kinetic laws of physical chemistry is by no means straighforward. Thus the equilibrium conditions required by thermodynamics are often difficult to obtain within a reasonable time-scale, and the rigorous kinetic treatment of systems that involve the transfer of dye from one phase to another (and in the case of reactive dyes, reaction with these phases) is necessarily complex. The situation may be further complicated by changes in the physical structure of the fibre during treatment at higher temperatures.

Accordingly a number of approximations is made in this book when dealing with the physical chemistry of dyeing systems, and theories developed for other physico-chemical systems and even biological ones have been applied to the specific problems of dyeing. This chapter provides an outline of the theoretical aspects of dye–fibre bonding, rates of dyeing and equilibrium affinity. For more detailed information, students should refer to the bibliography at the end of the chapter.

10.1 DYE–FIBRE BONDS
Broadly four types of chemical interaction are subsequently responsible for the substantivity of dyes for fibres. These are:
(a) Hydrogen bonds
(b) Van der Waals forces
(c) Electrostatic or ionic forces
(d) Covalent bonds.

The first three of these seldom act in isolation. However, depending on the dye and the fibre and the dyeing conditions, one of these physical forces of interaction will predominate. Additionally the so-called 'hydrophobic' interaction may be involved.

The hydrogen bond
A hydrogen atom attached to an electronegative atom, e.g. oxygen or nitrogen, can form a weak bond with another suitably placed electronegative atom. The most familiar example of this effect is seen in the properties of water, which has much higher melting and boiling points than would otherwise be expected, because its molecules are held together by hydrogen bonds (Figure 10.1).

Most fibres and dyes contain groups that can take part in this type of intermolecular combination. There is evidence for the importance of hydrogen bonds in dyeing certain fibres, e.g. cellulose acetates and possibly cellulosic and protein fibres.

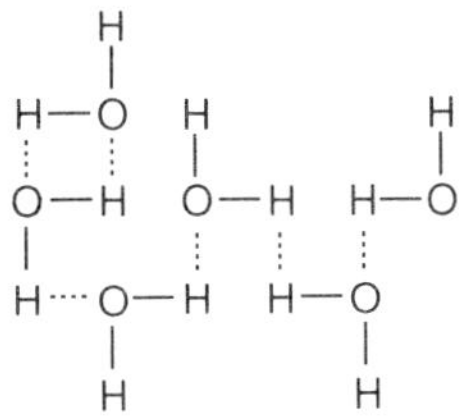

```
                H
                |
          H—O   H            H
          :     |            |
          O—H   O—H    H—O
          |     :      :
          H····O—H    H—O
                |           |
                H           H
```

Figure 10.1 – Hydrogen bonding in water

Hydrogen bonding may also play a role in the interaction of dye molecules with themselves (aggregation phenomena), and with certain surface-active agents used in dyeing processes. Intramolecular hydrogen bonding in dyes is a stabilising structural feature in connection with azo–hydrazo tautomerism and also with the light fastness of anthraquinonoid dyes (see section 9.2). Reduction in light fastness due to the presence of moisture may be caused by the disruption of intramolecular hydrogen bonds in the dyes.

A hydrogen bond in isolation is a relatively weak force (about 10-40 kJ/mol) and can be readily formed and broken. Because of the potential for intermolecular hydrogen bonding in many dye–fibre systems, numerous claims have been made for this type of interaction being important. Some of these claims have been based on heat (enthalpy) of dyeing ($\Delta H°$) values, which represent a quantitative measure of the strength of bonds between dye and fibre. Other factors can, however, contribute to $\Delta H°$ values and care must be exercised in interpreting them.

Van der Waals forces

These are a manifestation of the universal tendency of atoms and molecules to attract one another, and the van der Waals forces are usually divided into two types:

(a) Polarisation forces
(b) Dispersion or London forces.

Both dyes and fibres are polar molecules and as such can attract each other by their permanent dipoles or as a result of induced dipoles. The theory concerning the interaction energy between such molecules is outside the scope of this book, but it should be noted that these van der Waals polarisation forces fall off rapidly with distance of separation (theory predicts an inverse sixth-power relationship). Dye and fibre molecules must therefore approach each other very closely before mutual attraction exists, and lower-range repulsion forces may have to be overcome before this can happen.

Dispersion forces were first described by F London in 1930 to account for the fact that non-polar molecules and parts of molecules attract one another. Dispersion forces are relatively weak, but increase with molecular size (volume), becoming then relatively more effective than the polarisation type. This is important in the present context since both dye and fibre molecules are often large. Dispersion forces are also operative over a short range, and close alignment of long dye molecules with the long fibre axis is therefore important.

Van der Waals forces would therefore seem to be particularly effective in attracting a dye to a fibre when the two have certain special characteristics, e.g. either when they both have long and fairly flat molecules (as with cellulose and direct dyes or vat dyes and also with cellulose acetate and disperse dyes), or when both dye and fibre contain a considerable proportion of aliphatic or aromatic hydrocarbon groups (as with milling acid dyes applied to wool and disperse dyes applied to polyester). Polar and non-polar van der Waals forces also play an important part in dye aggregation, both in solution and in the fibre.

Electrostatic or ionic forces
A third form of physical attraction between a dye and a fibre may be due to a difference of
charge between them. In water all textile fibres become negatively charged and, since most
water-soluble dyes are anionic, adsorption does not occur readily. It is then necessary to
reduce or even reverse the charge on the fibre before the dye anion can approach closely
enough for attractive forces to become effective. (This does not apply with the use of
positively charged cationic dyes in the dyeing of acrylic fibres.)

Adding sodium chloride to the dyebath can have the required effect of reducing the
surface charge on cellulose, and acid is suitable with protein fibres and nylon. In the latter
case the mechanism involved in dyeing with levelling acid dyes in the presence of acid can
be illustrated as shown in Scheme 10.1. In water the amino and carboxyl groups of the wool
fibre are ionised, as shown by A. However, the ionised carboxyl and protonated amino
groups constitute a zwitterion, in which the positive and negative charges are balanced.
When the fibre is placed in the acidic dyebath, the acid is rapidly absorbed, its hydrogen
ion neutralising ('back-titrating') the carboxylate ions of the fibre, as shown by B. The result
is that the fibre becomes positively charged and negative ions are attracted to it. At first
the small, rapidly diffusing anions of the acid (X^-) enter and associate with the protonated
amino groups. Subsequently the larger, more slowly moving dye anions (D^-), which have
higher affinity, displace the acid anions, as shown by C, attachment of the dye anions to the
fibre being enhanced by the non-polar forces mentioned earlier.

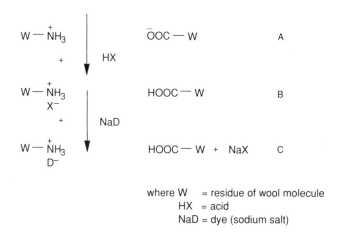

Scheme 10.1

The mechanism of the dyeing of acrylic fibres with basic (cationic) dyes has been
established as one of ion exchange whereby dye cations replace cations such as H^+, Na^+ or
K^+ which are attached to the acidic sites in the fibre. These strongly acidic sulphate (SO_4^{2-})
or sulphonate (SO_3^-) groups are introduced into the fibre as a result of redox catalysts used
in the polymerisation process. Weakly acidic carboxyl (COO^-) groups may also be present
from the use of comonomers in certain acrylic fibres.

If electrostatic forces alone were responsible for the binding of dyes in the nylon or wool/
levelling acid dye and acrylic/cationic dye systems, a correlation might be expected between
the amounts of dye adsorbed at equilibrium with the number of dye 'sites' in the fibre. Such
correlations have been reported for low molecular weight monobasic acid dyes on wool and

nylon, and certain cationic dyes on acrylics. In many cases, however, dyes are adsorbed in amounts in excess of that corresponding to the number of available sites. That such 'overdyeing' takes place suggests that other forms of binding (e.g. hydrogen bonding and van der Waals forces) are also operative.

Mention must be made at this point of 'hydrophobic' interaction. This is not strictly a new type of bond or force, but is due to two causes mentioned above acting simultaneously. Thus the van der Waals forces operating between hydrocarbon groups on the one hand, and the hydrogen bonds in water on the other, cause the respective assemblages of groups or molecules to associate together to the exclusion of the other. Dye–fibre attraction is promoted in this way since hydrocarbon groups in dyes will tend to be repelled from an aqueous environment and associate with similar groups in the fibre molecule. Although the phenomenon is normally used to explain the association of proteins in aqueous systems, the idea was first put forward by Meggy in connection with the bonding between wool and acid dyes [2].

Covalent bonds
Reactive dyes are attached to fibres by covalent bonds which are stronger than the previously mentioned forces and are difficult to break. Whereas van der Waals forces and hydrogen bonding are commonly considered to be physical interactions, the formation of a covalent bond between a dye and a fibre is a chemical reaction. In section 9.2 we have already seen how these reactions take place by nucleophilic substitution or nucleophilic addition, both well established mechanisms in organic chemistry. In the absence of the alkaline conditions required for the reaction, reactive dyes for cellulose generally have very low affinity for the fibre, due, for example, to the relatively small molecular size and non-planarity of such dyes, and other dye–fibre forces are unlikely to contribute in these cases.

With the reactive dyes used for wool, however, the chromogen system will possess some affinity for the fibre owing to the operation of electrostatic forces between dye and fibre, and other forces may also operate. In general the high wet fastness properties of reactive dyes can be attributed to the strength of the covalent dye–fibre bond, though with certain types of dye on cellulose, this bond is sensitive to acid hydrolysis and dyeings of poor fastness to water and perspiration may result. The fastness of reactive dyes on cellulosic fibres to chlorine and peroxide is also generally low.

10.2 RATE OF DYEING
A successful dyeing process can be conveniently broken down into three principal stages:
1. Diffusion of dye in the dyebath to the surface of the fibre
2. Adsorption of dye at the surface of the fibre
3. Diffusion of dye from the fibre surface to its interior.

As with any multi-stage process, the overall rate of reaction is determined by the slowest stage. In general stage 2 is almost instaneous, while stage 1 is faster than stage 3 (e.g. direct dyes have been shown to diffuse approximately 10^4 times faster in water than in cellulose), so that normally the overall rate of dyeing processes is determined by diffusion of dye within the fibre.

The low rate of diffusion of dye through the minute internal pores of the fibre and the tightness of the fibres or yarns in some types of fabric or package assemblies exercise restraint on dyeing; they tend to increase the time required for dyeing to be completed, i.e. for every fibre in the material to become evenly coloured right through to the centre. Thus, whereas under very favourable circumstances this dyeing time may be as low as a few minutes, or even seconds, it is normally an hour or more, and for some synthetic-polymer fibres, which have a very compact molecular structure, it may be as long as several days or weeks, unless special methods are used to accelerate dyeing.

Information on the kinetics of dyeing processes can be obtained using two different approaches:

(a) Measurement of the diffusion of the dye within the fibre; this concerns only stage 3 above
(b) Rate of dyeing curves (percentage exhaustion versus time), which relate to all three stages above.

Rate of dyeing measurements are experimentally easier to perform, while diffusion measurements give more fundamental information about the mechanism of the dyeing process. Both methods are considered below.

Diffusion measurements

Diffusion has been defined [3] as 'the process by which matter is transported from one part of a system to another as a result of random molecular motion'. The driving force in the dye diffusion process is the concentration gradient, the variation of dye concentration with distance through the fibre substrate, in much the same way as a potential gradient is the driving force in the passing of electric current. Fick's first law of diffusion (Eqn 10.1) relates the rate of transfer of solute (dye) per unit area of a diffusing material to the concentration gradient $(\partial c/\partial x)$:

$$F = -D \left(\frac{\partial c}{\partial x} \right) \tag{10.1}$$

where F = flux, or diffusional flux
       c = dye concentration
       x = distance through the substrate
       D = constant.

The constant of proportionality (D) in Eqn 10.1 is the diffusion coefficient, and in dyeing systems this is a measure of the diffusing properties of the dye (related to size and shape), the permeability of the fibre and intermolecular dye–fibre forces. The variation of dye concentration with time $(\partial c/\partial t)$ is of more significance since it more closely represents practical dyeing conditions, and is the basis of Fick's second law. In its simplest form this can be written as Eqn 10.2:

$$\frac{\partial c}{\partial t} = D \left(\frac{\partial^2 c}{\partial x^2} \right) \tag{10.2}$$

In practice the diffusion coefficient of a dye often varies with concentration (e.g. with direct dyes on cellulose and acid dyes on nylon) and Eqn 10.2 in these cases becomes Eqn 10.3:

$$\frac{\partial c}{\partial t} = \frac{\partial}{\partial x} \left(D \, \frac{\partial c}{\partial x} \right) \tag{10.3}$$

A full treatment of the derivation of these laws has been published [3]. Much investigative work on dye diffusion has been concerned with the determination of diffusion coefficients in an attempt to correlate these values with dye and fibre structure on the one hand, and with the overall rate of dyeing in real systems on the other. Most of the experimental methods for evaluating diffusion coefficients are complex and time-consuming, and as a result many kinetic studies on dye–fibre systems have taken the form of rate of dyeing measurements.

Rate of dyeing studies

At a given temperature, the amount of dye absorbed by the fibre can be measured with respect to time to give the familar rate of dyeing curve. The basis of such rate of dyeing studies is that there should be some relationship between the total amount of dye entering a fibre in a given time and the diffusion coefficient of the dye. Quantitatively such relationships can be derived by integration of Fick's second law expressions (Eqn 10.2 or 10.3). The solutions are all of the form of Eqn 8.18.

Values of c_t and c_∞ can be read off from a rate of dyeing curve, or determined by carrying out two identical dyeings, one to equilibrium and the other for time t. Tables of values of y (in Eqn 8.18) for corresponding values of c_t/c_∞ are available which allow the diffusion coefficient D to be evaluated, the values of l or r being known.

The derivation of expressions such as Eqn 8.18 involves a number of simplifying assumptions, which are not satisfied in real dyeing systems. These include the following:
(a) The conditions are those of an infinite dyebath, i.e. the concentration of dye at the surface of the substrate remains constant during dyeing (this is readily attainable under experimental conditions by ensuring that the volume of dye liquor is very large compared with that of the sample under test)
(b) The diffusion coefficient is constant. This is true only of certain disperse dye/synthetic fibre systems
(c) The complete surface of the fibre is accessible to dye molecules, and the diameter of each fibre in a group of fibres is constant.

The integrated diffusion equation is simplified by choosing the value of t to be the time of half dyeing ($t_{1/2}$) at which the percentage exhaustion is half that at equilibrium ($c_t/c_\infty = 0.5$). The diffusion coefficient is then given by Eqn 10.4:

$$D = \frac{0.0492\ l^2}{t_{1/2}} \qquad (10.4)$$

Eqn 10.4 applies to medium to long dyeing times and for small values of t Vickerstaff [1] gives the following approximation (Eqn 10.5):

$$\frac{c_t}{c_\infty} = 2\left(\frac{Dt}{\pi}\right)^{1/2} \qquad (10.5)$$

Thus a plot of c_t/c_∞ versus $t^{1/2}$ should be linear, with a slope proportional to $D^{1/2}$. This has been found to hold for a series of basic dyes on acrylic fibres.

Real systems

In practical dyeing situations the dyebath concentration decreases with time, i.e. the conditions are those of a finite dyebath. Integrated solutions of Fick's second law have been derived which relate to these conditions [4]. These solutions are more complex than those for infinite dyebath conditions, an important point being that they contain a factor that relates to the degree of exhaustion at equilibrium. The rate of dyeing therefore varies with the degree of exhaustion for a finite dyebath.

If we are comparing two or more dyes (e.g. for purposes of compatibility) using their rates of dyeing, the results are meaningless unless these measurements have been carried out to give the same values of equilibrium exhaustion for each dye. Such a comparison has been made [5] under conditions which gave 50% exhaustion (by varying electrolyte concentration) for each of a group of direct dyes on viscose yarn. It was therefore possible to compare the times of half dyeing $(t_{1/2})$ with diffusion coefficients obtained independently, i.e. a parameter derived from overall rate measurements with one derived from diffusion measurements.

Effect of temperature on dyeing systems

An increase in temperature increases the rate of any chemical reaction, e.g. above 50°C an increase of 10 degC will approximately double the rate of many reactions. The effect of a rise in temperature on dyeing systems is illustrated in Figure 10.2 and is two-fold:
(a) The rate of dyeing is increased
(b) The final equilibrium exhaustion is decreased.

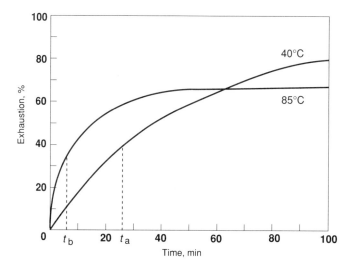

Figure 10.2 – Effect of temperature on rate of dyeing and equilibrium uptake; t_a and t_b are the respective times of half dyeing

Effect (b) is common with dye–fibre systems though it is not necessarily a universally observed one, and its occurrence indicates a negative value for the standard enthalpy of dyeing (ΔH°). The fact that, given sufficient time, more dye will be adsorbed onto a fibre dyed at the lower temperature has been made use of in a few cases where dyes for cellulose have poor exhaustion properties, e.g. 'cold-dyeing' vat dyes, solubilised vat dyes and naphthols used in azoic dyeing; these are all applied at low temperatures to achieve maximum exhaustion. Normally, however, dyeing at a low temperature is too slow to be practicable, and efficiency of exhaustion is sacrificed to speed of output by raising the temperature, usually to the boil or near it. Levelling by means of dye migration is also improved by this means. It has, in fact, been found advantageous in dyeing polyester fibres to use temperatures up to 130°C, considerably above the normal boiling point of water. This can be done only if the dyeing system is totally enclosed and heated under pressure (about 1 bar (15 lb/in^2) is produced by raising the temperature to 120°C), but the extra complication and expense that this entails are justified by the very considerable saving in time.

The effect of temperature on the rate constant (k) of a reaction is given quantitatively by the Arrhenius equation (Eqn 10.6):

$$\frac{\mathrm{d}\ln k}{\mathrm{d}T} = \frac{E}{RT^2} \tag{10.6}$$

where R = gas constant
E = energy of activation.

Activation energies of dyeing systems can be obtained from rate of dyeing measurements made under suitable conditions, i.e. by assuming that the rate constant is proportional to $1/t_{1/2}$ obtained from the rate of dyeing curve. A plot of log $t_{1/2}$ versus $1/T$ should give a straight line of slope $E/2.3R$ from which an 'activation energy of dyeing' can be calculated. The term E can be considered to be the amount by which the energy of activated dye molecules (those with sufficient energy to take part in the dye–fibre interaction) exceeds the average energy, and some values of E for different dyeing systems are shown in Table 10.1, from which the following important points emerge.

TABLE 10.1

Values of activation energy (E) for different dye–fibre systems [3]

Dye class	Fibre	E (kJ/mol)
Azoic coupling component	Viscose	42
Vat	Viscose	52
Direct	Viscose	59
Levelling acid	Wool	92
Milling acid	Wool	121
Disperse	Nylon	92
Disperse	Polypropylene	105
Disperse	Polyester	167
Basic	Acrylic	251

(a) The magnitude of E gives an approximate indication of the dyeing temperature used for the system, e.g. with low values of E (approx. 40 kJ/mol) dyeing can be carried out at room temperature. Values of around 130 kJ/mol require dyeing temperatures of about 100°C, while for those values above 140 kJ/mol, higher dyeing temperatures are required (e.g. 130°C for disperse dyes on polyester) or longer dyeing times at 100°C (e.g. basic dyes on acrylics).

(b) The magnitude of E also gives an indication of the mechanism of diffusion. Thus for low values the mechanism is usually one of adsorption onto, and migration along, capillary surfaces (e.g. cellulose systems). For very high values of E (140 kJ/mol and greater) it has been suggested that some sort of disruption of intermolecular polymer chains is required [3].

(c) From Eqn 10.6, dyeing rates involving a large value of E are very sensitive to small increases in temperature. It is not surprising therefore to find that this sort of sensitivity is evident with basic dyes on acrylics where the dyeing requirements are (in principle) controlled by a temperature rise of 0.5 degC/min between 80 and 100°C.

Diffusion in reactive dye–fibre systems

The diffusion behaviour of these dyes differs from other classes in that under certain pH conditions, reaction with the fibre (and water) takes place. The treatment of these systems is more complex and is outside the scope of this volume. Interested students will find the subject dealt with elsewhere [6].

10.3 THERMODYNAMICS OF DYEING (STANDARD AFFINITY AND HEAT OF DYEING)

The uptake of dyes from solution by textile substrates has been described in section 10.1 in terms of the formation of various types of dye–fibre bonds. This process is known as substantivity, which is defined (see Appendix A) as 'the attraction between a substrate and a dye or other substance under precise conditions of test where the latter is selectively extracted from the application medium by the substrate'. To obtain the quantitative measure of dye uptake, i.e. the affinity or standard affinity of the dye, requires the application of the principles of equilibrium thermodynamics to dyeing systems. This in turn requires a knowledge of the thermodynamic quantities that control equilibria in solution and solution–substrate systems. The relevant thermodynamic quantities include:

(a) The chemical potential (μ) of a dye in solution (μ_s) and in the fibre (μ_f) and their variation with dye concentration ([D])

(b) The standard affinity ($-\Delta\mu°$) of a dye defined in terms of the difference in the standard chemical potential of the dye in the fibre ($\mu°_f$) and that of the dye in solution ($\mu°_s$)

(c) The standard enthalpy change ($\Delta H°$), or heat of dyeing, determined from the variation with temperature of the dye uptake at equilibrium, which gives a measure of the strength of forces or bonds of attraction which bind the dye to the fibre

(d) The standard entropy change ($\Delta S°$) accompanying dyeing, determined from the variation of the standard affinity with temperature; this is (along with the enthalpy change) one of the driving forces leading to dye adsorption.

The quantities are related by the well known thermodynamic equation (Eqn 10.7):

$$\Delta\mu° = \Delta H° - T \Delta S° \qquad (10.7)$$

In the simplified treatment which follows, it is assumed that the chemical potential is related to dye concentration by Eqn 10.8:

$$\mu = \mu° + RT \ln[D] \qquad (10.8)$$

Complications arising from non-ideal behaviour (i.e. deviation from Eqn 10.8) are ignored and the treatment is thus restricted to dyeing systems which are free from ionic species. Thus for a dyeing system in which the dye is unionised in solution and on the fibre, e.g. disperse dyes on cellulose acetates, we can assume that a simple equilibrium exists at the end of a prolonged dyeing treatment between the amount of dye in solution, $[D]_s$, and that in the fibre, $[D]_f$. An equilibrium situation implies equality of chemical potential (Eqns 10.9 and 10.10):

$$\mu_s = \mu_f \tag{10.9}$$

$$\mu^\circ_s + RT \ \ln[D]_s = \mu^\circ_f + RT \ \ln[D]_f \tag{10.10}$$

We define the standard affinity of a dye by Eqns 10.11–10.13:

$$-\Delta\mu^\circ = -(\mu^\circ_f - \mu^\circ_s) \tag{10.11}$$

$$\therefore \quad -\Delta\mu^\circ = -RT \ \ln\frac{[D]_s}{[D]_f} = RT \ \ln\frac{[D]_f}{[D]_s} \tag{10.12}$$

$$-\Delta\mu^\circ = RT \ \ln K \tag{10.13}$$

where K is the distribution coefficient of the dye between the fibre and the dyebath solution.

The above treatment illustrates the derivation of the standard affinity for the ideal dyeing system where the dye is unionised in the solution and on the fibre. The closest approach in a real situation is the uptake of disperse dyes by hydrophobic polymers (e.g. cellulose acetate and polyester substrates). With other dye–fibre systems account must be taken of the contributions to the chemical potentials from the ionic species involved, e.g. Na^+, H^+ and dye ions. In the present work, studies are restricted to disperse dyes on cellulose acetate (section 8.5) and typically standard affinity $(-\Delta\mu^\circ)$ values are of the order of 25 kJ/mol, which imply a partition coefficient of about 2000:1. The sorption isotherms (concentration of dye on fibre plotted against dye concentration in solution at a fixed temperature) are typically linear over a wide range for disperse dyes on hydrophobic substrates, indicating that the distribution coefficient or partition ratio K is constant under these conditions. The relationship between K and $-\Delta\mu^\circ$ (e.g. for 100°C) is as shown in Table 10.2. Small changes in $-\Delta\mu^\circ$ can thus imply signficant changes in dye uptake.

TABLE 10.2

Partition ratio (K)	Standard affinity ($-\Delta\mu^\circ$) (kJ/mol)
10:1	7.14
100:1	14.3
1000:1	21.4
10000:1	28.5
100000:1	35.7

The enthalpy or heat of dyeing (ΔH°) is evaluated from the variation with temperature of either the distribution coefficient (K) or ($-\Delta\mu^\circ/T$). With the former variation the well known van't Hoff isochore is used (Eqn 10.14):

$$\frac{\mathrm{d}\ln K}{\mathrm{d}T} = \frac{\Delta H^{\circ}}{RT^{2}}$$

(10.14)

which in its integrated form, and assuming a constant ΔH°, can be written as Eqn 10.15:

$$\ln K = \frac{-\Delta H^{\circ}}{RT} + a$$

(10.15)

or, for measurement at only two temperatures (T_1 and T_2, with $T_2 > T_1$), by Eqn 10.16:

$$\ln \frac{K_2}{K_1} = \frac{\Delta H^{\circ}}{R}\left(\frac{T_2 - T_1}{T_1 T_2}\right)$$

(10.16)

which is a form of the equation used in the experiment in section 8.5.

Most dyes show a decrease in equilibrium uptake with increasing temperature, which implies a negative value of ΔH° and hence dyeing is an exothermic process. Values of heats of dyeing for disperse dyes on textile substrates lie in the range −20 to −60 kJ/mol, the magnitude indicating that a number of weak bonds may be involved.

In terms of the standard affinity, equations 10.14 and 10.15 can be expressed in the forms shown by Eqns 10.17 and 10.18:

$$\frac{\mathrm{d}\,(\Delta\mu^{\circ}/T)}{\mathrm{d}T} = \frac{\Delta H^{\circ}}{T^{2}}$$

(10.17)

$$\frac{-\Delta\mu^{\circ}}{T} = \frac{\Delta H^{\circ}}{T} + a$$

(10.18)

To evaluate ΔH° from measurements at several temperatures, a plot of $\ln K$ versus $1/T$ or $-\Delta\mu^{\circ}/T$ versus $1/T$ is prepared, and the slope of the linear plot is used to give ΔH°. The entropy of dyeing (ΔS°) can be evaluated from the variation of $-\Delta\mu^{\circ}$ with temperature (Eqn 10.19):

$$\Delta S^{\circ} = \frac{\mathrm{d}\,(-\Delta\mu^{\circ})}{\mathrm{d}T}$$

(10.19)

ΔS° can also be obtained from equation 10.7, given the values of $\Delta\mu^{\circ}$ and ΔH°.

The thermodynamics of dye–fibre systems is a complex subject and fuller treatments can be found in the references and bibliography to this chapter.

REFERENCES

1. T Vickerstaff, 'The physical chemistry of dyeing', 2nd Edn (Edinburgh: Oliver and Boyd, 1954).
2. P Rys and H Zollinger, 'Fundamentals of the chemistry and application of dyes' (New York: Wiley Inter-science, 1972); A.B. Meggy, J.S.D.C., **66** (1950) 510.
3. F Jones in 'The theory of coloration of textiles', Ed. A Johnson (Bradford: SDC, 1989) 373.
4. J Crank, J.S.D.C., **64** (1948) 384.
5. J Boulton, J.S.D.C., **60** (1944) 4.
6. I D Rattee, J.S.D.C., **85** (1969) 23.

BIBLIOGRAPHY

1. 'The theory of coloration of textiles', Ed. A Johnson (Bradford: SDC, 1989).
2. C L Bird, 'Theory and practice of wool dyeing', 4th Edn (Bradford: SDC, 1972).

11 LIGHT ABSORPTION AND REFLECTANCE BY COLOURED MATERIALS

Quantitative measurements of dye uptake can be made optically by measuring the light absorption characteristics of the dye remaining in the dyebath or by measuring changes in the light reflectance from the dyed material. Such measurements nowadays usually make use of a spectrophotometer operating over the visible region, i.e. over the wavelength range 400–700 nm, although simpler instruments using colour filters have been used in the past.

This chapter is concerned with the relationship of spectral character and colour, the laws relating light absorption and reflectance to dye concentration, the way in which instrumental measurements can be affected by differing solution and substrate conditions, and the basic components of the instruments used. The outline of the theoretical aspects given here should provide sufficient background for the interpretation of the results of appropriate experiments described in Chapter 8. Students needing a more detailed treatment should consult textbooks dealing with these subjects [1–4].

11.1 LIGHT ABSORPTION AND THE COLOUR OF DYE SOLUTIONS

A substance that is coloured in solution has the property of absorbing light selectively within the visible region. This absorption can be illustrated by recording the variation with wavelength of either transmittance (T) values or absorbance (A) values for the dye solution in a cell of fixed dimension, over the wavelength range 400–700 nm (which covers the visible region of the electromagnetic spectrum). It is, however, important to note that the absorbance is a logarithmic function of transmittance (Eqn 11.1):

$$A = \log\left(1/T\right) = \log\left(100\,/\,T\,\%\right) \tag{11.1}$$

The transmittance and absorbance curves of a purple solution of potassium permanganate are compared in Figure 11.1. The colour of the potassium permanganate solution under normal 'white' light or daylight conditions arises from the preferential absorption of the green wavelengths (approx. 480–600 nm) and the transmission of the rest; this gives a mixture of blue-violet (below 480 nm) and red (above 600 nm), which combined give the observed purple hue. The characteristics of light absorption curves are usually quoted in terms of the wavelength of maximum absorption (λ_{max}) and the spread of wavelengths ($\Delta\lambda$) at half A_{max}, i.e. the 'half bandwidth'; for the above potassium permanganate spectrum λ_{max} = 523 nm and $\Delta\lambda$ = 80 nm.

A typical set of absorption curves for yellow, red and blue acid dyes in water is illustrated in Figure 11.2. The dye concentrations used in making such measurements are often quite low (less than 0.05 g/l), which means that dyebaths usually have to be diluted for light absorption studies.

The relationship between light absorption and observed colour is a complex one and for dyes in solution will depend on the position, width, shape and intensity of the absorption curve in the visible region. Absorption often occurs over 100 nm half bandwidths, although the hue observed will depend principally on the λ_{max} position. Thus, in discussing the

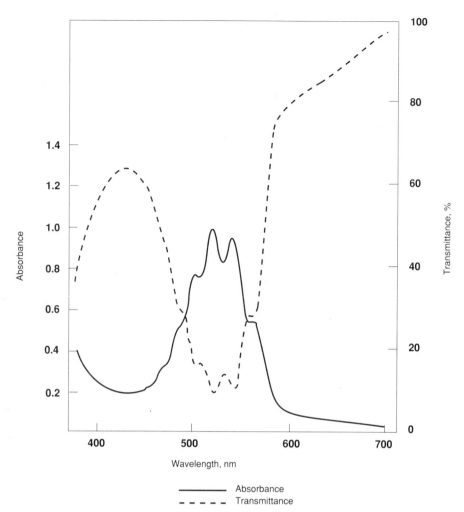

Figure 11.1 – Absorbance and transmittance curves of a solution of potassium permangante (KMnO₄)

TABLE 11.1

Absorption–hue relationships

Wavelength absorbed (λ_{max}) (nm)	Hue of light absorbed	Observed hue (of transmitted light)
400–440	Violet	Greenish-yellow
440–480	Blue	Yellow
480–510	Blue-green	Orange
510–540	Green	Red
540–570	Yellow-green	Purple
570–580	Yellow	Blue
580–610	Orange	Greenish-blue
610–700	Red	Blue-green

relationship between light absorption and the colour of solutions, tabulations of the type shown in Table 11.1 are often used. However, as illustrated in Figure 11.2, absorption curves of dyes often overlap considerably and a better representation is to show the spread of $\Delta\lambda$ values for dyes of varying hue; this method of representation is illustrated in Figure 11.3.

Finally, it was noted above that the intensity of light absorption contributes to the observed overall colour, and the following section discusses how we can quantify the intensity in terms of absorption coefficients (k or ε).

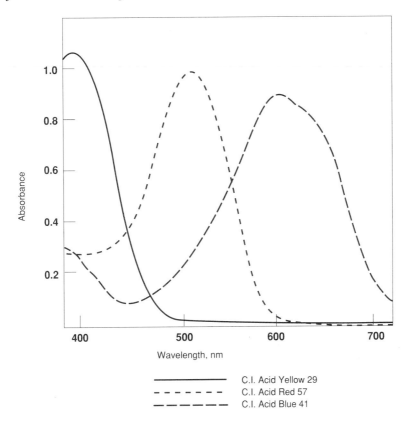

Figure 11.2 – Absorbance curves of acid dyes in water

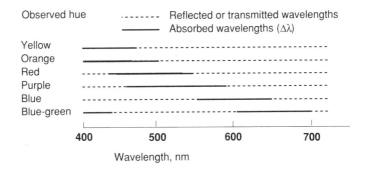

Figure 11.3 – Relationships between hue and half bandwidth ($\Delta\lambda$)

11.2 LIGHT ABSORPTION AND DYE CONCENTRATION (BEER'S LAW)

In the study of dyeing processes it is often necessary to follow the uptake of dye from the dyebath. This is usually done by diluting an aliquot of the dyebath with a suitable solvent and other additives to ensure a stable coloured solution, quantitatively measuring the absorption of radiation in a suitable part of the visible spectrum, and hence determining the concentration of the dye in the aliquot. By allowing for the dilution, the concentration of the dye in the sampled dyebath can be calculated.

For a single dye system the measurements of the light absorption can be carried out:
(a) By visual comparison methods
(b) Using a photoelectric filter absorptiometer
(c) Using a manual or recording spectrophotometer.

For mixtures of dyes it is necessary to use a spectrophotometer, and to test for additivity or non-additivity of dyes in the mixture as discussed in section 11.7.

In all quantitative studies of light absorption by dye solutions we make use of the laws of light absorption which apply to monochromatic radiation (in practice, light of a narrow band of wavelengths). Thus the theoretical basis of absorptiometric colorimetry is the Beer–Lambert law, summarising the respective discoveries of Bouguer (1729), Lambert (1760), and Beer (1852), which states that 'the absorption of light in passage through any medium is proportional to the number of absorbing entities in its path'. The mathematical form of this law can be written in a number of alternative forms, the most used having been given previously in Eqn 8.1.

The absorbance is defined in terms of the intensity of light passing through the sample cell (I_t) compared with the intensity passing through an identical cell filled with the solvent (the reference or blank cell) (I_0) (Figure 11.4). The absorbance can also be defined in terms of the transmittance (Eqns 11.1, 11.2 and Table 11.2):

$$T = I_t / I_0 \qquad A = \log (I_0 / I_t) = \log (1 / T) \tag{11.2}$$

Most spectrophotometers for the ultra-violet and visible regions are designed to give read-out values of absorbance between zero and 2.0 or in some cases 3.0, but solutions for testing are best kept within the range 0.2 to 1.5 absorbance units.

Figure 11.5 illustrates the absorbance and logarithmic absorbance plots for five concentrations of C.I. Acid Red 57 in water in 1 cm cells. Note that the logarithmic absorbance plots can be used to confirm identity (qualitative analysis) as the curve shape is independent of concentration (students should attempt to prove this from the Beer–Lambert law). The absorbance results can be used to construct a Beer's law calibration plot of absorbance versus concentration as illustrated in Figure 11.6.

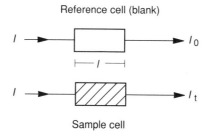

Figure 11.4 – Light transmission through spectrophotometric cells

TABLE 11.2

Absorbance	Transmittance (%)
0	100
0.301	50
1.00	10
2.00	1.0

With a high-quality spectrophotometer, linear plots should be obtained at all wavelengths in the region of absorption of the dye, although measurements are normally taken at the wavelength of maximum absorption (λ_{max}). This wavelength gives the Beer's law calibration graph of highest slope and hence at λ_{max} any error in the measurement of absorbance minimises the error in the value of concentration read off from the graph. However, when using less sophisticated filter instruments or spectrophotometers of wider measuring bandwidths, less satisfactory results are obtained if measuring away from the λ_{max} (Figure 11.7) and even the value of the absorbance at λ_{max} depends on the instrument used.

Hence Beer's law calibration graphs must be constructed for the instrument being used in any experiment where dye concentration is being determined by absorbance measurements (see experiment in section 8.1).

The slope of the Beer's law graph for solutions measured in 1 cm cells gives the absorption coefficient (k) or the molar absorption coefficient (ε), which are quantitative

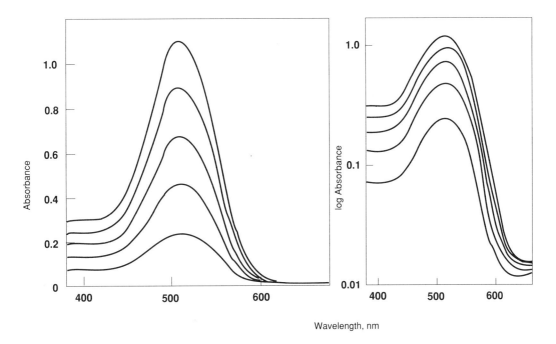

Figure 11.5 – Absorbance and log absorbance curves for C.I. Acid Red 57

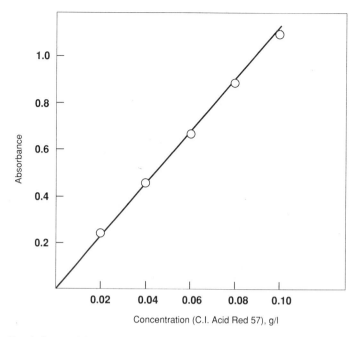

Figure 11.6 – Beer's law calibration plot at 510 nm

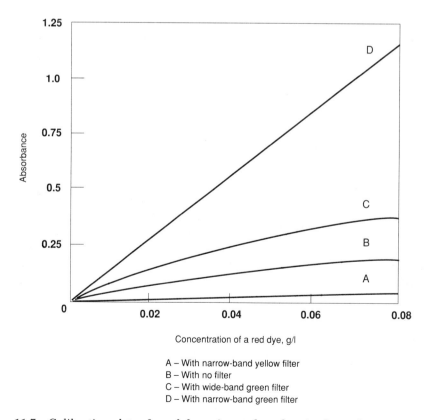

A – With narrow-band yellow filter
B – With no filter
C – With wide-band green filter
D – With narrow-band green filter

Figure 11.7 – Calibration plots of a red dye using a photoelectric absorptiometer

measures of the intensity of light absorption. Dyes are designed to show intense absorption and often have k values greater than 10 l/(g cm) (ε_{max} values greater than 10^4 l/(mol cm)) which accounts for the need to dilute dye solutions to less than 0.05 g/l (less than 10^{-4} mol/l) to give measurable absorbances in the range $A = 0.2-1.5$.

11.3 SOLUTION FACTORS AFFECTING DYE ABSORPTION SPECTRA

The colour of most dyes arises from electronic transitions occurring within the π-electron cloud of the chromogen. For the majority of dyes the external solution conditions can influence the electronic transitions and hence the absorption spectrum and the colour. A study of such effects can give information either about the properties of the dye or about the solution conditions. For example, measurements on acid–base indicators can be used to determine the dissocation constant of the indicator, but more usually the colour of the indicator is used to measure the pH of the solution.

Solution variables are also of importance from another viewpoint; unless they are controlled, qualitative and quantitative analyses are likely to be in error. A simple illustration of the problem is the determination of the concentration of phenolphthalein in water. If the standards for calibration were made up at pH 9, all would have a red colour and could be measured, say, at 500 nm on a visible region instrument. If, however, a phenolphthalein solution of unknown concentration had a pH of 3, it would be colourless and could not be determined by visible region spectrophotometry (i.e. in the range 400–700 nm).

In developing any method of qualitative or quantitative analysis it is necessary to assess the importance of each variable and to develop an analytical procedure which allows for, or minimises the effect of, the solution variables. For example, in the analysis of an indicator where the pH is uncontrolled, the measurements should be taken at the isosbestic point (see Fig 11.8) where the absorbance is independent of pH. Some of the more important solution factors are mentioned below although a more extensive treatment is given by Stearns [2].

Solvent effects

The molecular state of dyes and hence their absorption spectra can be influenced by choice of solvent. For example, direct dyes are often aggregated in aqueous solution, but the addition of pyridine reduces aggregation, and this is accompanied by a small change in the absorption spectrum. Similarly the spectrophotometric analysis of vat dyes can be carried out either on the reduced species in alkaline dithionite (hydrosulphite) solution or on the oxidised species in sulphuric acid, o-chlorophenol or pyridine as solvents. Aqueous acetone mixtures are used for analysing disperse dyes and the acetone content should be greater than 75% to ensure complete solubility and reproducibility of the absorption spectrum. Where a solvent effect is suspected, the conformity to Beer's law should be tested (section 8.1), and for mixtures the additivity of their spectra should be checked (section 11.7).

Effect of pH

A number of synthetic dyes and many of the natural dyes have substituent groups such as hydroxyl and amino attached to the main chromophoric system, which make the colour of these dyes sensitive to changes in pH. For example C.I. Acid Red 1 (LXIII) is yellower in alkaline solution while cochineal (LIX) is bluer in alkaline solution.

The colour changes which accompany the change in pH arise from the equilibria shown in Scheme 11.1, and these tend to occur over a pH range which depends on the equilibrium constants governing the acid (K_a) or base (K_b) ionisation behaviour of the dyes in question.

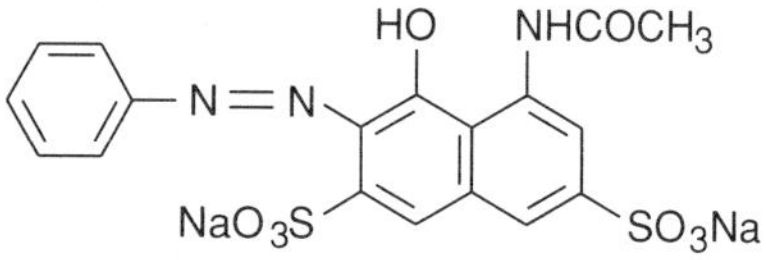

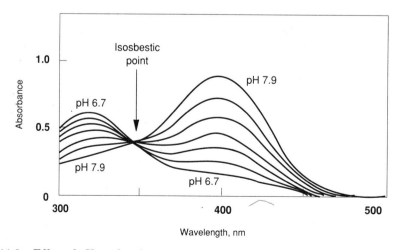

LXIII

$$R - OH \rightleftharpoons RO^- + H^+$$

or $$R - NH_3^+ \rightleftharpoons RNH_2 + H^+$$

acid form   alkaline form

Scheme 11.1

In terms of absorption spectra the changes can best be illustrated by the behaviour of acid–base indicator dyes, one of the simplest examples being *p*-nitrophenol, the behaviour of which is illustrated in Figure 11.8. These changes arise from the equilibrium shown in Scheme 11.2 for which we define the acid or indicator constant as given in Eqn 11.3:

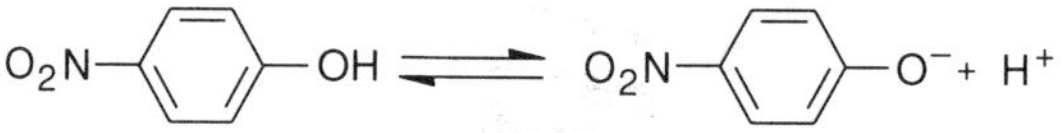

$$O_2N\!-\!\!\langle\ \rangle\!-\!OH \rightleftharpoons O_2N\!-\!\!\langle\ \rangle\!-\!O^- + H^+$$

HIn   In$^-$

Scheme 11.2

$$K_a = \frac{[RO^-][H^+]}{[ROH]} \quad \text{or} \quad K_{In} = \frac{[In^-][H^+]}{[HIn]} \tag{11.3}$$

Figure 11.8 – Effect of pH on the absorption spectrum of p-nitrophenol in aqueous solution

Analysis of the data of Figure 11.8 would show that K_{In} = 6.8 × 10^{-8} mol/l or pK_{In} = –log K_{In} = 7.2. The absorption curves of p-nitrophenol all pass through the same absorbance value at about 350 nm. This is known as the isosbestic point and arises because at this wavelength the molar absorption coefficients of the acid (HIn) and alkaline (In$^-$) forms are equal.

In the spectrophotometric analysis of pH-sensitive materials it is necessary to carry out the analysis at the isosbestic wavelength, or add sufficient acid or alkali to ensure that the equilibrium lies completely to one side or the other.

Other effects
Many other solution factors can influence the absorption spectra of dyes and the possibility of their influence should be considered when spectrophotometric methods of qualitative or quantitative analyses of dye solutions are being developed. The topic has been studied by Stearns [2] who discusses the following solution variables, giving examples of their influence on dye solutions:
– Solvent
– Hydrogen ion activity
– Concentration
– Temperature
– Heating of solution
– Interfering ions
– Ionic strength
– Irradiation
– Redox potential
– Dissolution aids
– Component interaction
– Hydrolysis
– Light fading
– Fluorescence
– Turbidity
– Plating.

11.4 LIGHT REFLECTANCE AND THE COLOUR OF DYED MATERIAL
A dye taken up by a textile substrate retains much of its light absorption properties and thus imparts an appropriate colour to the dyed material. Again the light absorption characteristics can be illustrated by recording the variation with wavelength of the reflectance, R, or some function of the reflectance (f(R)) which is a measure of the light absorption (and usually, like absorbance, is linearly related to the concentration of the dye on the substrate). However, the reflectance curve of a dyed substrate is usually broader or less sharp than the corresponding transmittance curve of the dye in solution. In addition there may be slight wavelength shifts corresponding to some difference in hue between solution and substrate and even between substrates. This substrate effect is illustrated for C.I. Disperse Violet 1 in Figure 11.9. With this dye the origin of the purple or violet hue observed can be explained in a similar way to that described in section 11.1 for potassium permanganate solutions.

Although relationships between spectral absorption and hue similar to those described before for dye solutions can be traced, the colour of dyed material can show significant differences in the other attributes of colour, i.e. lightness and saturation or chroma. Thus

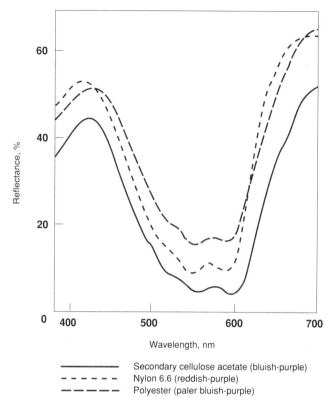

Figure 11.9 – Effect of substrate on the reflectance characteristics of C.I. Disperse Violet 1

white, grey and black differ only in lightness, and the reflectance curves for such colours are essentially flat, varying only in the mean reflectance. On the other hand, a white, cream and deep orange differ both in lightness and in chroma; the reflectance curves for such colours are illustrated in Figure 11.10. The more selective the absorption or reflectance of light, the higher is the chroma or saturation, whereas lightness depends mainly on the mean reflectance value and ranges from 100% for the ideal white to zero for the ideal black; a medium grey lies at 20% reflectance (see Chapter 12 for a discussion of colour attributes and specification).

11.5 LIGHT REFLECTANCE AND DYE CONCENTRATION (KUBELKA–MUNK FUNCTION)

Increasing the concentration or strength of the dye on a textile fabric results in a decrease in the reflectance, which is most marked at the wavelength usually corresponding closely to the λ_{max} of the dye in solution. A set of reflectance curves for C.I. Acid Red 57 on wool at different concentrations is shown in Figure 11.11. The reflectance is measured against a reference white such as pressed barium sulphate or magnesium oxide, and (like the transmittance) is a non-linear function of dye concentration. Various functions of reflectance have been suggested that give an approximately linear variation with concentration, and these include:

(a) The reciprocal of the reflectance
(b) The simplified Kubelka–Munk function (Eqn 8.2)

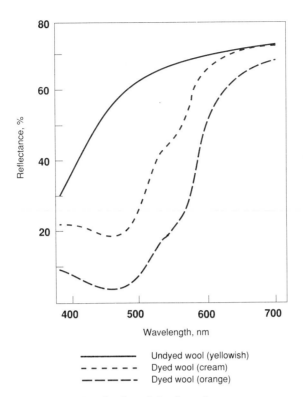

Figure 11.10 – Reflectance curves of undyed and dyed wool

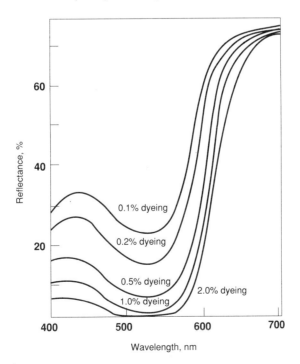

Figure 11.11 – Reflectance curves for C.I. Acid Red 57 on wool

(c) Other functions which include corrections for specular and surface reflection, e.g. Pineo and Saunderson equations [1].

The data from Figure 11.11 are plotted as the Kubelka–Munk function against concentration in Figure 11.12. This plot shows a reasonably linear variation with concentration, although, unlike absorbance versus concentration graphs, these may not pass through the origin and hence the relationship is written as Eqn 11.4 (see also Eqn. 8.3):

$$\mathrm{f}(R) = \mathrm{f}(R)_{\mathrm{w}} + \alpha c \tag{11.4}$$

where $\mathrm{f}(R)_{\mathrm{w}}$ is the Kubelka–Munk function for the undyed substrate, and α is an absorption coefficient, which varies with wavelength.

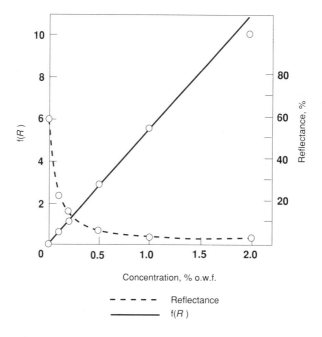

Figure 11.12 – Reflectance and Kubelka–Munk plots for C.I. Acid Red 57 at 525 nm

The wavelength variation of the absorption coefficient of C.I. Acid Red 57 on wool is compared in Figure 11.13 with the absorption curve of the same dye in aqueous solution. The shape of log $\mathrm{f}(R)$ versus wavelength curves, like log A curves for a dye in solution, is independent of concentration and can be used to check the identity of a single dye on a substrate.

11.6 FACTORS AFFECTING LIGHT REFLECTANCE
The measurement of light reflectance using a spectrophotometer requires the use of a reflectance sampling device in which the direction of illuminating and viewing of the sample can vary from one instrument to another. However, the aperture, reference white and preparation of the sample for measurement all require to be closely specified for reproducible measurements. Complications can be introduced by surface texture, orienta-

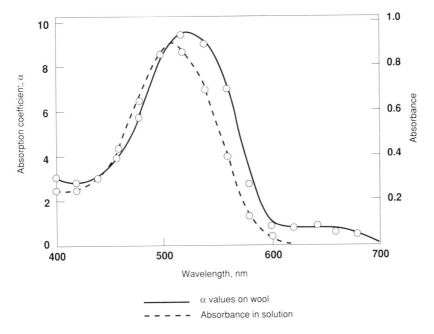

Figure 11.13 – Absorption coefficient of C.I. Acid Red 57 on wool and in solution

tion and fluorescence effects. If the last-mentioned is present the recorded reflectance will depend on the position of the sampling device in the optical train of the instrument (section 11.8). Significant deviations from the linearity of the Kubelka–Munk function can arise at high dye concentrations, mainly due to the importance of surface reflection contributions (at low reflectances).

Most of these effects are beyond the scope of the present text but are discussed in detail elsewhere [5].

11.7 SPECTROPHOTOMETRIC ANALYSIS OF DYE MIXTURES

The analysis of a mixture of two or more dyes in solution depends on the system fulfilling a number of criteria:

(a) The absorption curves of the component dyes in the mixture should be as dissimilar as possible

(b) The component dyes should not interact, so that at any wavelength the absorbance of the mixture is the sum of the absorbances of the components (this can readily be tested by preparing known mixtures)

(c) Each of the component dyes should individually obey Beer's law and the absorption coefficients (k) need to be known at the optimum wavelengths for the analysis (at n wavelengths for n components). The choice of optimum wavelengths is made so that the absorption coefficients of the components are as different as possible (for a two- or three-component mixture, the λ_{max} value for each dye is often chosen, provided these are sufficiently far apart).

Thus for a two-component mixture measured in 10 mm cells ($l = 1$ cm), the absorbance values ($A_{a,m}$ and $A_{b,m}$) for the mixture at λ_a and λ_b respectively are given by Eqns 11.5 and 11.6:

$$\text{At } \lambda_a \quad A_{a,m} = A_{a,1} + A_{a,2} = k_{a,1}c_1 + k_{a,2}c_2 \tag{11.5}$$

$$\text{At } \lambda_b \quad A_{b,m} = A_{b,1} + A_{b,2} = k_{b,1} c_1 + k_{b,2} c_2 \tag{11.6}$$

These two simultaneous equations can be solved to find c_1 and c_2, i.e. the mixture can be analysed. Similar arguments can be applied to the analysis of dyed material using Eqn 11.4. The accuracy of the analysis depends on the care with which the samples are presented for measurement, and on checking the blank solution or reference white at each of the analytical wavelengths. The accuracy diminishes as the number of components is increased and/or as the absorption curves approach one another.

For three-component mixtures measurements are taken at three optimum wavelengths to give Eqns 11.7–11.9:

$$\text{At } \lambda_a \quad A_{a,m} = k_{a,1} c_1 + k_{a,2} c_2 + k_{a,3} c_3 \tag{11.7}$$

$$\text{At } \lambda_b \quad A_{b,m} = k_{b,1} c_1 + k_{b,2} c_2 + k_{b,3} c_3 \tag{11.8}$$

$$\text{At } \lambda_c \quad A_{c,m} = k_{c,1} c_1 + k_{c,2} c_2 + k_{c,3} c_3 \tag{11.9}$$

The required concentrations are then given by the following determinants (Eqns 11.10–11.12):

$$c_1 = \begin{vmatrix} A_{a,m} & A_{b,m} & A_{c,m} \\ k_{a,2} & k_{b,2} & k_{c,2} \\ k_{a,3} & k_{b,3} & k_{c,3} \end{vmatrix} \div K \tag{11.10}$$

$$c_2 = \begin{vmatrix} k_{a,1} & k_{b,1} & k_{c,1} \\ A_{a,m} & A_{b,m} & A_{c,m} \\ k_{a,3} & k_{b,3} & k_{c,3} \end{vmatrix} \div K \tag{11.11}$$

$$c_3 = \begin{vmatrix} k_{a,1} & k_{b,1} & k_{c,1} \\ k_{a,2} & k_{b,2} & k_{c,2} \\ A_{a,m} & A_{b,m} & A_{c,m} \end{vmatrix} \div K \tag{11.12}$$

$$\text{where } K = \begin{vmatrix} k_{a,1} & k_{b,1} & k_{c,1} \\ k_{a,2} & k_{b,2} & k_{c,2} \\ k_{a,3} & k_{b,3} & k_{c,3} \end{vmatrix}$$

One way of obtaining the solution to the above equations is to use matrix algebra, and this can be performed readily nowadays in many computer systems. In matrix form the equations are written as Eqn 11.13:

$$\boldsymbol{A} = \boldsymbol{KC} \tag{11.13}$$

where the vector A contains all the absorbances $A_1 \ldots A_n$ of the mixture and the vector C the concentrations $c_1 \ldots c_n$; the matrix K denotes all the absorption coefficients. It follows that Eqn 11.14 can be written:

$$C = K^{-1}A \qquad (11.14)$$

where the inverse of the matrix K^{-1} is easily calculated by standard methods of matrix algebra.

The simple nature of the matrix algebra in computer form is illustrated below by the program instructions required for the three-component analysis in the MINITAB statistical package (most computer systems have statistical packages that can handle matrix manipulations of this type).

For a three-component system
READ 3 by 3 matrix M1
(Type in k values into DATA rows (3 off)
READ 3 by 1 matrix M2
(Type in absorbance values of mixture in three rows of DATA)
INVERT M1 to M3
MULTIPLY M3 by M2 and put into M4
PRINT M4 (this gives the calculated concentrations).

11.8 INSTRUMENTS FOR MEASURING LIGHT ABSORPTION/REFLECTANCE

Visual comparison techniques provide the simplest method of determining the concentration of coloured materials in solution, and the earliest instruments developed for such measurements used the visual comparison principle. Even today certain types of colorimetric analyses make use of the visual comparison of a solution colour with the simulated colour produced by a coloured glass disc or filter (e.g. the Lovibond colour comparator). For a single dye it is possible to place a series of solutions of known concentrations in test tubes and to compare the dyebath being analysed in a similar tube placed side by side with each member of the calibration series in turn to give an estimate of the dye concentration, which with care can be done to within ±5% accuracy.

However, in most studies today use is made of prism or grating spectrophotometers that are capable of measuring absorbance, and, via suitable calibration graphs or calibration data held electronically within the instrument, of analysing for dye concentrations to within ±1% accuracy. The basic elements in all such instruments are as illustrated in Figure 11.14.

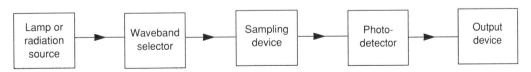

Figure 11.14 – Basic elements of a spectrophotometer

The precise nature and layout of the components varies from instrument to instrument, and the particular features and characteristics of any instrument used in the practical sections of this book should be noted [1]. In the sections below some of the variations which can arise from the use of instruments with different characteristics are described.

When using light absorption as a method of analysing dye solutions it is usual to adjust the waveband selector (colour filter, prism or grating monochromator) so that the particular coloured light chosen is absorbed strongly by the dye solution being analysed. The magnitude of this absorption is determined by the absorption coefficient, which depends on the dye being studied. However, the precise value of the absorbance of a solution of a known dye at a known concentration depends on a number of instrumental factors:
(a) The wavelength or hue of the incident light
(b) The spread of wavelengths (the waveband width) in the incident light beam
(c) The proportion of 'stray light' in the incident beam
(d) The effective path length of the incident light through the sample cell.

Wavelength calibration
For a given instrument any calibration graph will be reproducible provided the instrumental characteristics do not change. One possible source of error is a change in wavelength calibration and this should be routinely checked according to the instrument's instruction manual. For a spectrophotometer that operates in the visible region a quick check can be done by eye by observing the colour of the light emerging from the exit slit of the monochromator. When observing a 'true' yellow (i.e. with neither greenish nor reddish hue) the wavelength will, for those with normal colour vision, lie in the region of 575–579 nm. Hence any error in excess of 5 nm can be quickly spotted by this method. Wavelength errors can produce significant errors in absorbance, particularly if measuring at a sharp absorption maximum or on the sloping sides of an absorption band.

Wavelength errors are unlikely to occur with coloured filters unless the filter becomes damaged or is replaced. In the latter situation new calibration data should be prepared.

Effect of bandwidth
The influence of bandwidth is an important cause of variation, again when measuring sharp absorption curves or on the sloping side of an absorption curve. Many filter instruments have bandwidths of the order of 30 nm or more, whilst even simple spectrophotometers (e.g. with a wedge interference monochromator) may have bandwidths of the order of 10 nm or more. The modern high-quality spectrophotometer will normally be operated at slit widths corresponding to 1 nm or less. Significant differences in bandwidth or slit width give rise to appreciable differences in the slopes of calibration data (see section 8.1 and Figure 11.7).

Stray radiation
This is defined as radiation reaching the detector that is not normally expected in the measuring beam with the wavelength and waveband settings being used. It can arise from dust on the optical components, poor optical design, etc. It is most noticed near the wavelength limits of the instrument and causes non-linearity in Beer's law plots [2].

Sample cells and effective path length
The quality of sample cells can vary widely and for the highest quality work in the visible region matched glass cells of accurately known path length should be used. However, for most dyeing experiments the cheaper plastic cells are adequate.

Where the measuring beam in an instrument is focussed within the sample compartment, deviation from Lambert's law can occur if the faces of the cell are not held at right angles to the principal direction of the incident light beam.

Reflectance spectrophotometers

Many of the high-quality spectrophotometers can be adapted for reflectance measurements by placing a reflectance device in the sampling area. Such devices are usually of the integrating spheroid type [1] in which the incident light beam is directed onto the surface of the coloured sample being examined, whilst the reference light beam is similarly directed at a known angle on to a reference white surface (usually a pressed sample of barium sulphate or magnesium oxide, or a white tile). The diffusely reflected light is collected by the integrating sphere and passed to the detector for a comparison or ratio measurement of the percentage reflectance.

It is important in such measurements to have a reproducible method of sample preparation and presentation, particularly for textile materials such as yarns; it is also important to take care of the white reference surface and to renew it from time to time. The actual reflectance value recorded will depend on the optics of the reflectance device and in particular on the illuminating angle and viewing geometry, as well as on the aperture characteristics. With an integrating sphere there is often the choice of including or excluding the specular (or mirror-like) component with the appropriate use of a gloss trap and this should be noted in quoting results.

For fluorescent samples the optical train needs to be altered with the light from the source falling directly onto the sample, and the waveband selector or monochromator being used to analyse the reflected light. This order of optical components is used in the modern rapid-scan diode array spectrometer; details of such instruments and of the more traditional types are given elsewhere [1].

REFERENCES

1. D Patterson in 'Colour physics for industry', Ed. R McDonald (Bradford: SDC, 1987) 35.
2. E I Stearns, 'The practice of absorption spectrophotometry' (New York: Wiley Interscience, 1969).
3. 'Practical absorption spectrometry', Vol. 3 – Techniques in visible and ultra-violet spectrometry, Ed. A Knowles and C Burgess (London: Chapman Hall, 1984).
4. R C Denney and R S Sinclair, 'Visible and ultra-violet spectroscopy' in the series 'Analytical chemistry by open learning' (Chichester: John Wiley, 1987).
5. R McDonald in 'Colour physics for industry', Ed. R McDonald (Bradford: SDC, 1987) 116.

12 COLOUR SPECIFICATION AND MEASUREMENT

The results of dyeing experiments are usually described in terms of the nature of the colour or change in colour produced. Unfortunately verbal descriptions of colour can be ambiguous and the terms used to describe colour change can vary from one industry to another. This chapter starts with a description of general colour terminology, and then deals with some of the specific terms used in the dyeing industry; Appendix A lists the definitions and meanings of some of the more important colour terms used in the dyeing industry. However, in many situations instrumental colour measurements are replacing and/or supplementing verbal descriptions, and the bases of the 1931 CIE and the 1976 CIELAB colour specification systems are described. The final sections deal with some applications of instrumental colour measurement including colour-difference assessment and computer colour matching procedures.

Several textbooks on colour measurement have been published in recent years and can be recommended for further reading [1–3].

12.1 COLOUR DESCRIPTIONS AND THE COLOUR SOLID

The colour of an object can be described in the simplest way by referring only to the hue, i.e. by saying that the object is blue, yellow, red, brown, etc. However, if we wish the description to be more meaningful we often use hue qualifiers such as pale, deep, reddish, etc. Alternatively we may use a specific colour name such as lilac, turquoise, scarlet. These names are associated with reasonably well defined colours, but nowadays manufacturers of coloured goods often devise their own specific colour names that may be the product of the fertile imagination of a sales promotion team! To be of any value as colour descriptions it is essential that specific colour names are illustrated by the use of colour samples or standards. Most manufacturers produce colour charts or colour cards to illustrate their range of coloured products, and list the colour names used.

It is recognised that three variables can be distinguished for surface colours i.e.:
– Hue, H
– Lightness, L
– Chroma or saturation, C.

The hue variable is readily understood and allows us to distinguish reds from blues, greens, etc. Lightness is that attribute of colour which distinguishes light colours from dark colours and whites from greys and blacks. The third term describes the purity of colour and is zero for whites, greys and black but increases to a maximum with vivid colours such as those shown by flowers or highly chromatic pigments and dyes. It is possible to arrange a series of coloured chips in the form of a colour solid or three-dimensional array in terms of these three attributes as illustrated in Figure 12.1.

Many collections, such as the Munsell and the Methuen books of colour, utilise this type of arrangement with the hues being on different pages of the colour book or atlas, whilst within a page colour chips are arranged to show variations in lightness and chroma or a combination of these two variables. The lightness axis represents the black to white or dark to light variation, whilst the chroma axis represents increasing saturation from the neutral

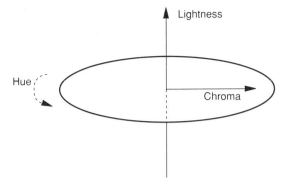

Figure 12.1 – Three-dimensional colour solid

axis out to the most vivid colours. The specification of a colour in such systems will be a three-part specification defining the hue page and the lightness and chroma values within that page, e.g. a Munsell specification of a pink colour might be 2.5RP 6/4. The relationships between hue qualifiers and the variables of lightness and chroma are illustrated in Figure 12.2. Full details of such colour atlases and specifications can be found in the publications of the National Bureau of Standards (NBS) and the Inter-Society Color Council of America (ISCC) and elsewhere [3].

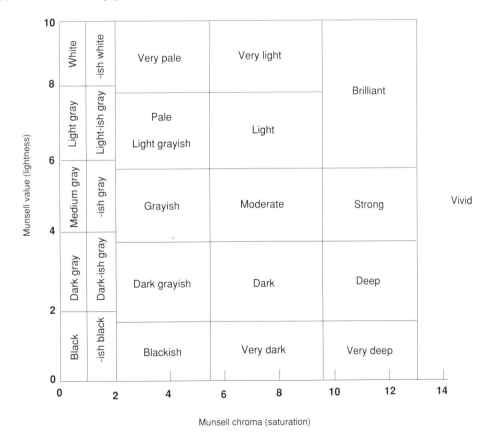

Figure 12.2 – Munsell coordinates and hue qualifiers

The most recent edition of the ISCC–NBS colour names dictionary is published under the title *Color – universal language and dictionary of names*. Here the concept of six levels of 'fineness' of colour designation is introduced. It ranges from level 1, in which only 13 divisions of the colour solid are recognised (each identified by a simple hue term) to level 6, in which approximately five million divisions of the colour solid are defined by quoting CIE coordinates to three significant figures, or by giving an interpolated Munsell specification to the same precision. Table 12.1 is reproduced from the above publication, where the type and examples of colour designations are illustrated for each of the six levels of the Universal Color Language (UCL). It is claimed that the UCL is being used increasingly in science, education, art and industry, particularly because it is an open-ended system, i.e. extendable to a seventh level when occasion demands.

TABLE 12.1

Fineness of colour designation	Colour name designation			Numeral and/or letter colour designations		
	Level 1[a]	Level 2	Level 3	Level 4	Level 5	Level 6[b]
Number of divisions of colour solid	13	29	267	943–7056	$\approx$100 000	$\approx$5 000 000
Type of colour designation	Generic hue names and neutrals	All hue names and neutrals	ISSC–NBS; all hue names and neutrals with modifiers (NBS-C553)	Colour-order systems (collections of colour standards sampling the colour solid systematically)	Visually interpolated Munsell notation from *Munsell book of colour*	CIE (x, y, Y) or instrumentally interpolated Munsell notation
Example of colour designation	Brown	Yellowish-brown	Light yellowish-brown	Munsell 1548 10YR 6/4	9.5 YR 6.4/4.25	$x = 0.395$ $y = 0.382$ $Y = 35.6\%$ or 9.6YR 6.45/4.3

(a) Least precise
(b) Most precise

One of the useful features of the above publication is the dictionary of colour names and descriptions derived from a number of well known colour order systems (collections of colour standards) such as the Maerz and Paul Colour Atlas, the Colour Harmony Manual, the Textile Colour Card Association, the Horticultural Colour Chart, etc. These colour names are keyed to the ISCC colour descriptions and the Munsell colour coordinates, which in turn can be related to the CIE coordinates (section 12.3).

12.2 COLOUR-DIFFERENCE TERMS USED IN THE COLOUR INDUSTRIES

In the colour-using industries different terms from the above will be used to describe colours, or more particularly colour differences. For example, the terms used in the textile dyeing industry are given in Table 12.2. There is no disagreement about the hue difference terms but many alternatives occur for the strength and brightness ones. A recent survey has shown that the preferences are for the terms 'fuller' or 'thinner' to indicate 'strength' variations, and 'brighter' or 'flatter' to indicate brightness variations. The variables of strength and brightness are associated with changes in both lightness and saturation in the way depicted in Figure 12.3. The precise orientation of these axes in colour space depends on the actual colours being examined, as will be seen later. In the paint and pigment industries a greater number of variables is used (Figure 12.4)

TABLE 12.2

Colour term	Colour-difference terms
Hue or shade	Bluer, yellower, greener, redder, etc.
Strength or amount of dye	Weaker, stronger, paler, fuller, deeper
Brightness	Brighter, duller, flatter, greyer

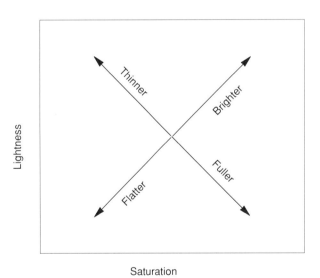

Figure 12.3 – Colour variables used in the dyeing industry

12.3 1931 CIE AND 1976 CIELAB COLOUR SPECIFICATIONS

In Chapter 11 the relationships between spectral absorption, transmittance or reflectance and perceived colour were discussed briefly. Such relationships can be interpreted in terms of the stimulation of the red, green and blue cone receptors in the human eye [1]. However, the standard international method of colour specification, first accepted by the Commission Internationale de l'Éclairage (CIE) in 1931 is based on the principles of additive mixing of

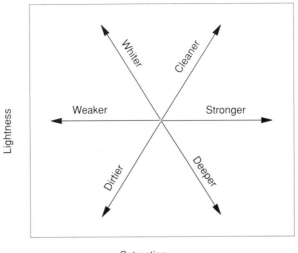

Figure 12.4 – Colour variables used in the paint and pigment industries

coloured red, green and blue lights and defines colour in terms of three tristimulus values X, Y and Z. For opaque coloured objects these values are defined by Eqns 12.1–12.3:

$$X = \int S(\lambda)\,\bar{x}(\lambda)\,R(\lambda)\,\mathrm{d}\lambda \tag{12.1}$$

$$Y = \int S(\lambda)\,\bar{y}(\lambda)\,R(\lambda)\,\mathrm{d}\lambda \tag{12.2}$$

$$Z = \int S(\lambda)\,\bar{z}(\lambda)\,R(\lambda)\,\mathrm{d}\lambda \tag{12.3}$$

where $S(\lambda)$ represents the spectral power of some standard illuminant, $\bar{x}(\lambda)$, $\bar{y}(\lambda)$ and $\bar{z}(\lambda)$ the spectral response characteristics of one of the two standard observers (2° or 10°) and $R(\lambda)$ is the spectral reflectance characteristics of the coloured object. In practice these integrations are replaced by summations (see section 8.9).

For the present purposes the tristimulus XYZ values give an indication of the extent of reflection respectively in the red, green and blue regions of the visible spectrum, with the ideal white having $X = Y = Z = 100$ and the ideal black $X = Y = Z = 0$. A medium grey under daylight (bluish) illumination will have the approximate values $X = 20$, $Y = 20$, $Z = 21$. Colours can be represented in the 1931 chromaticity diagram in which the chromaticity co-ordinates are defined by $x = X/(X + Y + Z)$, $y = Y/(X + Y + Z)$ (See Figures 2.1 and 12.5).

The 1931 CIE chromaticity diagram is illustrated in Figure 12.5 with the boundary representing the chromaticity coordinates of pure spectral light sources. This boundary is well outside that of real surface colours. Thus most surface colours have much lower purity or chroma (are less vivid) than spectral light sources and are therefore represented in the central areas of the chromaticity diagram. The third dimension of lightness is represented by the Y value, so that the 1931 CIE specification is often of the form x, y, Y; e.g. the light brown colour in Table 12.1 has the specification $x = 0.395$, $y = 0.382$, $Y = 35.6$.

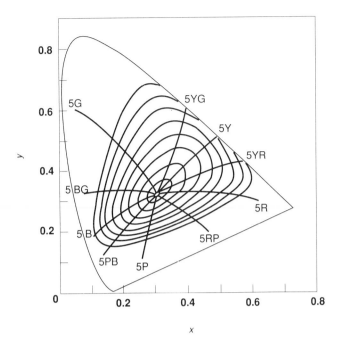

Figure 12.5 – 1931 CIE chromaticity diagram showing Munsell hue and chroma loci

One of the disadvantages of the 1931 CIE colour space for commercial and industrial applications of colour measurement and colour-difference assessment is that the colour space is visually non-uniform, as illustrated by the irregular spacing of the Munsell hue lines and chroma loci in Figure 12.5. Over the years many modifications of the *XYZ* values have been tried as the basis of a set of coordinates defining a visually uniform colour space. One of the modifications accepted by the CIE in 1976, defining CIELAB (1976) colour space, utilises Eqns 2.2–2.4. In these equations the X_o, Y_o and Z_o values are the tristimulus values of a reference white under the particular standard illuminant chosen (see section 12.5).

The CIELAB chromaticity (*a*b*) diagram or colour map is shown in Figures 2.2 and 12.6 and the latter incorporates the Munsell hue lines and chroma loci. The circular nature of the latter and the more uniform spacing of the hue lines compared with Figure 12.5 indicates the improved visual uniformity of the 1976 CIELAB space over the 1931 version.

Colours in CIELAB space can also be defined in terms of polar co-ordinates (Eqns 2.2, 12.4 and 12.5):

Metric hue angle

$$h = \arctan (b*/a*) \qquad (12.4)$$

Metric chroma

$$C* = [(a*)^2 + (b*)^2]^{1/2} \qquad (12.5)$$

These polar coordinates are claimed to be directly correlated with the visual attributes of colour, namely hue, lightness and chroma. However, their main use in the textile dyeing industry is to quantify colour differences, as discussed below.

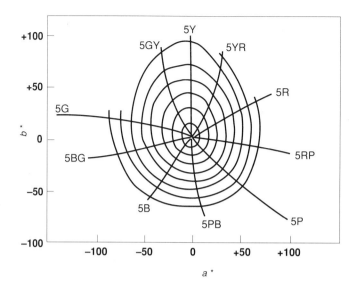

Figure 12.6 – 1976 CIELAB chromaticity diagram showing Munsell hue and chroma loci

12.4 COLOUR-DIFFERENCE MEASUREMENTS (ΔE VALUES)

In industrial dyeing practice it is important to have personnel or procedures that allow decisions to be made about the acceptability or otherwise of the colour of a dyed batch of material when it is assessed against the standard that defines the target colour. This has been done traditionally by visual assessment using experienced colourists (section 2.3) and it is only within recent years, with the advent of reliable instrumentation, that it has become possible to consider replacing visual with instrumental assessment. One additional development, which was necessary before instrumental assessments could be used in industry, was that of a colour-difference formula that showed a high correlation with visual assessment. Although final agreement has still to be reached internationally, the CIELAB colour-difference equation has been widely used by industry, but for the most critical work this has been superseded in the UK by a formula based on the work of McDonald, which has been further developed by the Colour Measurement Committee of the Society of Dyers and Colourists (the CMC equation) [1].

The magnitude of the colour difference (ΔE) in CIELAB space is defined by the length of the line between the L^*, a^* and b^* coordinates of two points representing the colours being compared (see Eqn 2.5), or in terms of polar coordinates, Eqn 12.6:

$$\Delta E = [(\Delta L^*)^2 + (\Delta C^*)^2 + (\Delta H^*)^2]^{1/2} \tag{12.6}$$

The modified CMC (l:c) equation current in 1987 is given in Eqn 12.7:

$$\Delta E = \left[\left(\frac{\Delta L^*}{l S_\mathrm{L}}\right)^2 + \left(\frac{\Delta C^*}{c S_\mathrm{C}}\right)^2 + \left(\frac{\Delta H^*}{S_\mathrm{H}}\right)^2\right]^{1/2} \tag{12.7}$$

where $S_\mathrm{L} = 0.040975 L_1^* / (1 + 0.017654 L_1^*)$

unless $L_1{}^* < 16$ when $S_L = 0.511$
$$S_C = 0.0638C_1{}^*/0.0131C_1{}^* + 0.638$$
$$S_H = S_C(Tf + 1 - f)$$
$$f = \{(C_1{}^*)^4/[(C_1{}^*)^4 + 1900]\}^{1/2}$$
$$T = 0.36 + [0.4 \cos(h_1 + 35)]$$

unless h_1 is between $164°$ and $345°$ when $T = 0.56 + [(0.2 \cos(h_1 + 168)]$

$L_1{}^*$, $C_1{}^*$ and h_1 refer to the standard of a pair of samples, these values and ΔL^*, ΔC^* and ΔH^* being calculated from the CIELAB formulae.

The constants in the CMC equation were fixed so that when l and c are set at unity (CMC 1:1), the equation is the most reliable developed so far for quantifying the perceptibility of small colour differences, i.e. up to ten CIELAB units. In judging the perceptibility of colour difference, equal importance is given to differences in lightness, chroma and hue.

The magnitude of ΔE values and the relationship to semi-quantitative estimates of colour difference used in the colour industries are best illustrated by the standard grey scale used for assessing the change of colour during fastness testing (Table 12.3).

TABLE 12.3

Grey scale	ΔE(CIELAB)	ΔE(ANLAB)[a]	Magnitude description
5	0	0	No difference
4	1.7	1.5	Slight
3	3.4	3.0	Little
2	6.8	6.0	Some
1	13.6	12.0	Much

(a) The grey scale was originally defined in terms of the *Lab* coordinates of the Adams–Nickerson colour space [1]

12.5 VISUAL COLOUR MATCHING AND METAMERIC INDICES

In an industrial dyehouse facilities for the visual assessment of dyed material against a standard sample must be provided. Traditionally such colour matching was done at a north-facing well lit window by an experienced colourist or dyer. However, the variability of natural daylight and the limitation of colour matching to daylight hours resulted in a demand for standardised colour matching cabinets using defined light sources, which was answered by the issue of a British Standard, i.e. BS950 Part 1 (1967) defining 'artificial daylight for the assessment of colour'.

This standard defines spectral and colorimetric characteristics for 'artificial daylight' sources, the level of illumination required and the background colour of the matching cabinet (neutral grey of 15% reflectance is suitable for routine colour matching work). Commercial colour matching cabinets have been designed to meet with the above specifications, although where visual colour matching of the highest standard is required it is important to monitor regularly the lamp output and spatial distribution of illumination levels across the colour matching area.

Most commercial colour matching cabinets provide a selection of light sources in addition to the 'artificial daylight' source (which is an approximation to the CIE standard D_{65} illuminant). These additional sources usually include a tungsten source (approximating to CIE standard A illuminant), an ultra-violet (u.v.) lamp for assessing fluorescent samples, and often 'cool white' or other fluorescent tubes to simulate average indoor lighting characteristics. It is normal practice to check the quality of a colour match under at least two light sources, and if there is a change in the quality of the colour match under these conditions to qualify the colour match as being 'metameric'. Metamerism arises when the dyed sample and standard possess different reflectance curves but show similar colour under one illuminant, and usually occurs when the sample and standard are dyed using different combinations of dyes. Under these conditions disagreement about the quality of a colour match will inevitably arise as such matches are not only illuminant dependent but are also observer dependent. It is possible to quantify the degree of illuminant metamerism using instrumental measurements. Thus the CIELAB values can be computed under both illuminant A and illuminant D_{65} and the corresponding colour difference (ΔE) values calculated. A metameric index can then be defined (Eqn 12.8):

$$(MI) = \Delta E (A) - \Delta E (D_{65}) \tag{12.8}$$

and of course if the samples match under illuminant D_{65} [ΔE (D_{65}) = 0], then Eqn 12.9 is valid:

$$(MI) = \Delta E(A) \tag{12.9}$$

This simple index of metamerism is used in computer colour matching procedures (see below).

In most of the experiments listed in Part II of this manual the results require to be assessed visually and the colour or colour change described. The colour matching conditions should be noted, and, where appropriate, standardised descriptions or instrumental measurements of the colour or colour difference quoted.

Those responsible for employing and training personnel for the dyeing industry need to be aware of the possibility of an observer having defective colour vision. About 8% of the male population, but only about 0.5% of females, are found to have defective colour vision, principally resulting in reduced or zero discrimination in the red/green region. It is important that personnel being selected for dyeing, or other work in which good colour discrimination is required, are screened for defective colour vision. Various simple screening tests are available such as the Ishihara book of pseudo-isochromatic plates (PIC tests), which are based on the use of coloured dot patterns on a coloured dot background, using colours which are confused by observers with red/green deficiencies. However, to characterise fully an observer's colour vision a battery of colour vision tests needs to be applied including PIC tests, the Munsell–Farnsworth 100-hue test, tests with an anomaloscope and even the Color Aptitude test, which assesses the ability of an observer to discriminate small differences in chroma using plastic chips. Full details of the subject of defective colour vision and methods of testing have been dealt with in detail elsewhere [1].

It is sufficient here to emphasise that prospective employees and students should be screened at an early stage for defective colour vision, and that such screening should only be carried out under recommended conditions by persons experienced in the testing procedures. It might also be mentioned that various medical conditions including alcoholism and diabetes can give rise to acquired defective colour vision rather than inherited defective colour vision. Any such observed onset of defective colour vision requires medical advice on its significance.

12.6 COMPUTER COLOUR MATCHING (INSTRUMENTAL MATCH PREDICTION)

An outline of the procedures used in computer colour matching (CCM) is indicated in the flow diagram of the experiment in section 8.10. The two steps which are essential to the success of the procedure are:

(a) The calculation of the reflectance curve for any mixture of three chosen dyes
(b) The evaluation of correction coefficients which allow the initial arbitary recipe to be adjusted.

The calculation of the reflectance curve for a three-dye mixture makes use of the additivity of the Kubelka–Munk function as indicated by Eqn 12.10:

$$\mathrm{f}(R) = \mathrm{f}(R)_{\mathrm{w}} + \alpha_1 c_1 + \alpha_2 c_2 + \alpha_3 c_3 \tag{12.10}$$

where α_1, α_2 and α_3 are the absorption coefficients for the three dyes used in admixture. These need to be available from calibration dyeings and require measurements across the visible spectrum (usually 16 values for each dye at 20 nm intervals from 400 to 700 nm inclusive). The accuracy of a colour matching procedure depends critically on the quality of the calibration data and the linearity of the reflectance function ($\mathrm{f}(R)$) over the concentration region of interest. Methods of dealing with non-linearity are reviewed by McDonald [1].

For a three-dye mixture a total of nine correction coefficients require to be evaluated, i.e. $(\partial c_1/\partial X)$, $(\partial c_1/\partial Y)$, $(\partial c_1/\partial Z)$, $(\partial c_2/\partial X)$, $(\partial c_2/\partial Y)$, $(\partial c_2/\partial Z)$, $(\partial c_3/\partial X)$, $(\partial c_3/\partial Y)$ and $(\partial c_3/\partial Z)$.

The steps in the evaluation of these coefficients are indicated in the annotated version of the CCM program (Appendix B) used in the experiment in section 8.10, whilst the background theory is given in McDonald [1]. The evaluation of the correction coefficients requires use of the absorption or calibration coefficients (α_1, α_2 and α_3) and a matrix inversion procedure. The correction coefficients are of course the partial derivatives of the variation of dye concentrations with X, Y and Z and hence, if we can evaluate the difference between the desired X, Y, Z values and those calculated by the computer program from the initial arbitary concentrations, we have a method for evaluating the change (Δc_1) in dye concentration required (Eqn 12.11):

$$\Delta c_1 = \left(\frac{\partial c_1}{\partial X}\right)\Delta X + \left(\frac{\partial c_1}{\partial Y}\right)\Delta Y + \left(\frac{\partial c_1}{\partial Z}\right)\Delta Z \tag{12.11}$$

and similarly for Δc_2 and Δc_3.

Computer colour matching procedures are now widely available in the textile dyeing industry. They not only provide trial recipes quickly and effectively, but can be used to select the optimum dye combination for recipe preparation, minimise cost and metamerism and provide formulation methods for blending stock-dyed fibres to produce the required colour in a blended fibre system. The computer can also be used for inventory control of dyes and chemicals and for other dyehouse management functions. Several studies [1] have examined the cost-effectiveness of computer prediction systems, and all have demonstrated that such installations are not only cost-effective but are also essential in the modern industrial dyehouse.

REFERENCES

1. 'Colour physics for industry', Ed. R McDonald (Bradford: SDC, 1987).
2. K McLaren, 'The colour science of dyes and pigments', 2nd Edn (Bristol: Adam Hilger, 1980).
3. F W Billmeyer and M Saltzman, 'Principles of color technology', 2nd Edn (New York: John Wiley, 1983).

APPENDIX A

Selected entries from *Colour terms and definitions*, published by the Society of Dyers and Colourists (1988)

Absorption spectrum The curve relating the absorption of radiant energy by a substance (usually in solution) to the wavelength of the radiant energy. *Note*: Absorption spectra relating to certain parts of the total radiant energy spectrum are often described specifically, e.g. ultra-violet spectrum and infra-red spectrum.

Acid dye An *anionic dye* characterised by *substantivity* for protein fibres and often applied from an acid dyebath.

Affinity The quantitative expression of *substantivity*. It is the difference between the chemical potential of the dye in its standard state in the fibre and the corresponding chemical potential in the dyebath. *Note*: Affinity is usually expressed in units of joules (or calories) per mole. Use of this term in a qualitative sense, synonymous with substantivity, is deprecated.

Afterchrome process A method of dyeing in which the fibre is dyed with a *mordant dye* and afterwards treated with a chromium compound to form a dye–chromium complex within the fibre.

Anionic dye A dye that dissociates in aqueous solution to give a negatively charged coloured ion.

Auxiliary A chemical or formulated product which enables a processing operation in preparation, dyeing, printing or finishing to be carried out more effectively or which is essential if a given effect is to be obtained.

Auxochrome A substituent group in a *chromogen* that influences its colour

Azoic composition A mechanical mixture of an azoic coupling component and an azoic diazo component. *Note*: The azoic diazo component is a diazotised primary amine present as a diazo compound that is chemically passive when in neutral or alkaline aqueous solution at normal temperatures but becomes reactive when heated or treated with acid.

Azoic dyeing The production of an insoluble azo compound on a substrate by interaction of a diazotised amine (azoic diazo component) and a coupling component (azoic coupling component).

Backtanning An aftertreatment to improve the wet fastness of dyed or printed silk or polyamide materials, using either natural or synthetic tanning agents.

Barry (barré) Descriptive of faulty fabrics that exhibit light and dark bars across the fabric. These may originate in, for example,. differences in lustre, dyeing behaviour or pick spacing.

Basic dye A cationic dye characterised by its *substantivity* for the acidic types of acrylic fibre and for tannin mordanted cotton.

Batchwise processing Processing of materials as lots or batches in which the whole of each batch is subjected to one stage of the process at a time (see also *continuous process*).

Bathochcromic effect An effect by which the *absorption spectrum* of a substance is shifted to a longer wavelength part of the spectrum.

Blocking agent A restraining agent specifically intended to control the absorption of dye by one or more components of a multi-component fibre system.

Carrier A type of accelerant particularly used in the dyeing or printing of hydrophobic fibres with disperse dyes.

Cationic dye A dye that dissociates in aqueous solution to give a positively charged coloured ion (see also *basic dye*).

Chromaticity coordinates Two numbers (denoted x and y) which together represent in the CIE (Commission Internationale de l'Éclairage) system the colour quality.

Chromaticity diagram A geometrical method of representing the colour quality of a coloured object by the position of a point on a two-dimensional grid. *Note*: Since colour is a three-dimensional quantity, it is also necessary to specify the luminance of the coloured object to obtain a complete specification of its colour.

Chrome dye A *mordant dye* capable of forming a chelate complex with a chromium ion.

Chromogen A chemical compound that is either coloured or can be made coloured by the attachment of suitable substituents. The *chromophore* and the *auxochrome(s)* are part of the chromogen.

Chromophore A chemical group which when present in a compound (the *chromogen*) is responsible for the appearance of colour. *Colorants* are sometimes classified on the basis of their chief chromophore, e.g. azo dyes contain the chromophore $-N=N-$.

Colorant A colouring matter, a *dye* or *pigment*. *Note*: This noun is recommended as a generic term.

Colour (1) (sensation) That characteristic of the visual sensation which enables the eye to distinguish differences in its quality, such as may be caused by differences in spatial distribution or fluctuations with time.
(2) (of an object) The particular visual sensation (as defined above) caused by the light emitted by, transmitted through, or reflected from the object. *Note*: The colour of a non-self-

luminous object is dependent on the spectral composition of the incident light, the spectral reflectance or transmittance of the object and the spectral response of the observer. Colour can be described approximately in terms of *hue, saturation*, and *lightness*, or specified numerically by *chromaticity coordinates*, e.g. those defined by the CIE standard observer data (1931). Alternatively, colour can be specified by reference to visual standards, e.g. the Munsell Color Atlas.

Colour Index An authoritative, descriptive catalogue of natural and synthetic *colorants* and intermediates in terms of generic name, and constitution where disclosed.

Colour solid That part of colour space occupied by surface colours.

Colour temperature (of a light source) The temperature at which a full radiator would emit radiation of substantially the same spectral distribution in the visible region as the radiation from the light source and which would therefore have the same *colour*. *Note*: Colour temperature refers only to a source of light and not to a reflecting surface.

Colour triangle A type of *chromaticity diagram*.

Colour value The colour yield of a *colorant* compared with a standard of equal cost. *Note*: It is usually determined by comparing the cost of coloration at equal strength. Comparisons are normally made between products of similar *hue* and properties.

Colour yield The depth of colour obtained when a standard weight of *colorant* is applied to a substrate under specified conditions.

Compatibility value (K) A value used to characterise *basic dyes* according to their compatibility for use in the dyeing of acrylic fibres. Dyes of equal *K* value are compatible dyes under practical *exhaust dyeing* conditions except when *acid dyes* or *auxiliaries* are present.

Continuous process A process in which material passes in sequence through a series of stages to give a continuous output of processed material.

Couple To combine a suitable organic component, usually a phenol or an arylamine, with a diazonium salt to form an azo compound as in the manufacture of azo colorants in *azoic dyeing* or in the aftertreatment of direct dyeings.

Depth That *colour quality* an increase in which is associated with an increase in the quantity of *colorant* present, all other conditions (viewing, etc.) remaining the same.

Detergent A substance normally having surface-active properties specifically intended to cleanse a substrate.

Diffusion (1) Movement of substances owing to the existence of a chemical potential gradient usually caused by a variation in concentration.
(2) (in photographic processing) The *migration* of developing or other reagents within a layer, or from one layer to another, in a photographic emulsion.

Direct dye An *anionic dye* having *substantivity* for cellulosic fibres, normally applied from an aqueous dyebath containing an electrolyte.

Disperse dye A substantially water-insoluble dye having *substantivity* for one or more hydrophobic fibres, e.g. cellulose acetate, and usually applied from fine aqueous dispersion.

Dullness (of a colour) That colour quality, an increase in which is comparable to the effect of the addition of a small quantity of neutral grey *colorant*, whereby a match cannot be made by adjusting the strength. *Note* It is generally found that an increase in dullness is accompanied by a decrease in both *saturation* and *lightness*.

Exhaust dyeing (1) A batchwise dyeing process in which the dyebath is discarded on completion as opposed to the use of a standing bath.
(2) A second dyeing carried out to determine the degree of exhaustion of a dyebath. *Note*: This is normally a laboratory test. On completion of dyeing, the dyed material is removed from the dyebath and replaced by undyed material. Dyeing is then continued for a further period; this is the 'exhaust dyeing' which, by comparison with the original dyeing, indicates the degree of exhaustion of the original dyebath.

Exhaustion The proportion of dye or other substance taken up by a substrate at any stage of a process to the amount originally available.

Fade (1) In fastness testing, any change in the *colour* of an object caused by light or contaminants in the atmosphere, e.g. burnt-gas fumes. *Note*: The change in colour may be in *hue, depth* or brightness or any combination of these.
(2) Colloquially, a reduction in the depth of colour of an object irrespective of cause.

Grey scale A series of neutrally coloured chips, showing increasing contrast within pairs, used visually to assess contrasts between other pairs of patterns: for example, the ISO (International Organisation for Standardisation) grey scales comprise two series of chips against which the magnitude of change in colour of a specimen submitted to a fastness test and of staining of adjacent uncoloured material can be visually assessed and rated on a 1 to 5 scale (see also BS1006:1978).

High-temperature dyeing (HT dyeing) Dyeing under super atmospheric pressure whereby the temperature of the dye liquor is raised above its normal boiling point. *Note*: The use of the term 'pressure dyeing' in this connection is deprecated.

Hue That attribute of *colour* whereby it is recognised as being predominantly red, green, blue, yellow, violet, brown, etc.

Hypsochromic effect An effect by which an *absorption spectrum* of a substance moves to a shorter wavelength part of the spectrum.

Ingrain dye A *colorant* which is formed *in situ* in the substrate by the development and coupling of one or more intermediate compounds. *Note*: The term was originally used for colorants obtained from oxidation bases and by azoic techniques, but is now reserved for other types of colorant formed *in situ*.

Leuco dye A reduced form of a dye from which the original dye may be regenerated by oxidation (see *vat dye* and *sulphur dye*).

Levelling *Migration* of dye leading to a more uniform coloration of a substrate.

Levelling acid dye An acid dye that migrates readily when applied to wool by the optimum method for that dye (see report of the Committee on the Dyeing Properties of Wool Dyes, J.S.D.C., **66** (1950) 213).

Levelling agent Strictly, a substance that, added to the dyebath, promotes *levelling*. *Note*: This term is also widely used to describe substances that do not necessarily promote *levelling* but which do assist level dyeing.

Light Radiant energy capable of stimulating the eye and causing the sensation of vision. *Note*: Radiation near to the ends of the visible spectrum is sometimes referred to as light, e.g. ultra-violet light, instead of radiation. This is deprecated.

Lightness That property of a coloured object by which it judged to reflect or transmit a greater or a smaller proportion of the incident light than another object (see *colour*).

Liquor:goods ratio (liquor ratio or LR) The ratio of the weight of liquor employed in any treatment to the weight of material treated. *Note*: 'Short' and 'long' are often used to describe low and high liquor:goods ratios, respectively.

Listing An undesirable variation of colour across the width of a dyed fabric.

Luminance The *luminous flux* emitted per unit solid angle or per unit projected area of a real or imaginary surface. *Note*: For a coloured object, luminance is a measure of the apparent overall reflectance. For a light source, luminance is a measure of the apparent brightness of the light.

Luminous flux The summation over all visible wavelengths of the product of radiant energy of a given wavelength emitted per unit time and the relative visual response of the standard observer to radiation of that wavelength (see *standard observer data*).

Mass coloration (1) A method of colouring man-made fibres by incorporation of the *colorant* in the spinning composition before extrusion into filaments.
(2) A method of colouring plastics by incorporation of the colorant before the final product is formed.

Match Two or more objects that are judged to be very similar in *colour*.

Matching A process by which the amount of each colouring matter present in a material is adjusted so that the final *colour* resembles that of a given sample as closely as possible.

Metal-complex dye A dye having a coordinated metal atom in its molecule. *Note* : Unless the term 'metal-complex dye' is used in direct association with a particular application class of dye, e.g. 'metal-complex disperse dye' or 'metal-complex reactive dye', its use is deprecated.

Metamerism A phenomenon whereby the nature of the colour difference between two similarly coloured objects changes with change in the spectral distribution (characteristics) of the illuminant. *Note 1* Metamerism is most frequently seen when two coloured objects match in daylight, but differ markedly in colour when viewed in tungsten-filament light. This arises because the visible absorption spectra of the two objects differ significantly, although the *tristimulus values* in daylight are identical. *Note 2* This term is often used loosely to describe the behaviour of a single coloured object that shows a marked change of colour as the illuminant changes. Use of the term in this way is incorrect; this effect should be described as lack of colour constancy.

Migration The movement of a dye or pigment from one part of material to another. *Note*: It may be desirable (see *levelling*) or undesirable.

Milling acid dye An *acid dye* of good fastness to acid or alkaline milling.

Mordant A substance, usually a metallic compound, applied to a substrate to form a complex with a dye which is retained by the substrate more firmly than the dye itself.

Mordant dye A dye that is fixed with a *mordant*.

Onium dye A cationic dye that is solubilised by a labile ammonium, sulphonium, phosphonium or oxonium substituent which splits off during fixation to leave an insoluble *colorant* in the fibre.

Padding Impregnation of a substrate with a liquor or a paste, followed by squeezing, usually by passage through a nip to leave a specific quantity of liquor or paste on the substrate. *Note*: This term is often used as a synonym for slop padding.

Pigment A substance in particulate form which is substantially insoluble in a medium, but which can be mechanically dispersed in this medium to modify its *colour* and/or light-scattering properties.

Potting A finishing process for wool fabric to give specific smooth handle. *Note*: A roll of fabric is treated in water at 70 to 100°C for several hours, then allowed to cool slowly and finally immersed in cold water.

Rate of dyeing The rate at which a dye is absorbed by a substrate under specified conditions. *Note*: It may be expressed quantitatively in several ways, such as the weight of dye absorbed in unit time, or the time taken for the substrate to absorb a given fraction of the amount of dye which it will absorb at equilibrium.

Reactive dye A dye that, under suitable conditions, is capable of reacting chemically with a substrate to form a covalent dye–substrate linkage.

Reflectance curve A plot against wavelength of the fraction of the incident light (or other radiation) reflected by an object at each wavelength in the spectrum.

Retarding agent A substance that, added to a dyebath, reduces the *rate of dyeing*, but does not substantially affect the equilibrium *exhaustion* (synonymous with 'retarder').

Salt sensitivity (1) The extent to which the dyeing properties of a dye are affected by an addition of neutral electrolyte to the dyebath. *Note*: This term is usually only applied in the dyeing of cellulosic fibres.
(2) The susceptibility of coloured material to change in colour when spotted with aqueous solutions of neutral electrolytes.

Saturation (of a colour) The nearness of *colour* in purity to the associated *spectral colour*.

Saturation value The maximum quantity of a dye which can be absorbed by a substrate under defined conditions.

Scouring Freeing textile materials or wool sheepskins from natural or other non-fibrous constituents by treatment with aqueous solutions or organic solvents.

Setting (1) The process of conferring dimensional and/or shape stability on fibres, yarns or fabrics by means of moist or dry heat, or in leather mechanically. *Note*: The operation of setting is applied to textile materials of all kinds but assumes special significance in the treatment of thermoplastic materials. Setting is usually accompanied by changes in the fibre which may affect its coloration properties.
(2) The drying of a paint or varnish film to a point where for all practical purposed it ceases to flow.
(3) The initial drying of a printed ink film.

Shade (noun) A common term loosely employed to describe broadly a particular *colour* or *depth*, e.g. pale shade, 2% shade, mode shade and fashion shade.

Shade (verb) To bring about relatively small modifications in the *colour* of a substrate by adding a further small amount of *colorant* with the object of matching a given pattern more accurately.

Skitteriness An undesirable speckled effect arising from differences in colour between adjacent fibres or portions of the same fibre.

Solubilised sulphur dye A thiosulphuric acid derivative of a *sulphur dye* which during dyeing is converted to the substantive alkali-soluble thiol form.

Solubilised vat dye A water-soluble salt of the sulphuric ester of a leuco *vat dye*. *Note*: After application to the fibre the parent vat dye is regenerated by hydrolysis and oxidation.

Spectrophotometer An instrument, usually photoelectric, for measuring the reflectance or transmittance of light (or other radiation) by an object at a particular wavelength in the spectrum.

Staining (1) An undesirable local discoloration.
(2) Coloration of non-textiles by surface application of a coloured solution or dispersion.
(3) In fastness testing of coloured textiles, the transfer of colorant from the test material to the adjacent materials (see 'Standard methods for the determination of colour fastness of textiles and leather', 4th Edn [Bradford: Society of Dyers and Colourists, 1978] and supplements).
(4) In textile printing, the soiling of whites in the washing process.
(5) (Paper) A method of colouring paper as an after-process by treating it in the web with a dye solution.

Standard observer data In the CIE system of colour measurement, the relative amounts of three defined stimuli, mixed additively, required by the average observer to match spectral light at each wavelength under defined viewing conditions.

Strength (1) (of a dye) The *colour yield* of a given quantity of dye in relation to an arbitrarily chosen standard.
(2) (of a dyeing or print) Synonymous with *depth*. *Note*: The terms stronger and weaker are used in a different sense in colorimetry to denote more or less saturation in measured colour differences.

Strike (1) The uptake of dye by a substrate from a dyebath in the early stages of dyeing.
(2) The result of the first period of dyeing, especially in wool dyeing.

Stripping Destroying or removing *dye* or finish from a fibre.

Substantivity The attraction between a substrate and a dye or other substance under the precise conditions of test whereby the latter is selectively extracted from the application medium by the substrate.

Sulphur dye A dye, containing sulphur both as an integral part of the *chromophore* and in attached polysulphide chains, normally applied in the alkali-soluble reduced (leuco) form from a sodium sulphide solution and subsequently oxidised to the insoluble form in the fibre.

Surfactant An agent, soluble or dispersible in a liquid, which reduces the surface tension of the liquid (a contraction of 'surface-active agent').

Tailing A dyeing fault consisting of a gradual change in colour along a length of material to which *colorant* has been applied by padding or other continuous technique.

Temperature-range properties (of a dye) The extent to which the *depth* produced by a dye under specified application conditions is affected by a change of temperature.

Tippy wool Wool in which the tip portions of the fibres have been so damaged by weathering during growth as to have markedly different dyeing properties.

Tristimulus colorimeter An instrument (usually photoelectric) designed to measure the colour of an object directly in terms of the *tristimulus values*.

Tristimulus values (of a coloured object) The amounts of three defined primaries (usually blue, red and green) required to be mixed additively to match the *colour* of the object, under defined conditions.

Vat dye A water-insoluble dye, usually containing keto groups, which is normally applied to the fibre from an alkaline aqueous solution of the reduced enol (leuco) form, and which is subsequently oxidised in the fibre to the insoluble form.

APPENDIX B

Simple computer colour matching program in BASIC

```
>LIST
   10 REM COMPUTER COLOUR MATCHING PROGRAM
   20 W=1
   30 PRINT "GIVE REQUIRED X,Y,Z VALUES"
   40 INPUT X1,Y1,Z1
   50 PRINT "GIVE STARTING VALUES OF C1,C2,C3"
   55 INPUT C1,C2,C3
   70 DIM A(3,3),B(3,3),C(3,3)
   75 PRINT "        C.I. ACID DYES"
   77 PRINT "YEL 29    RED 57    BLUE 41    X      Y      Z"
   80 DIM K(16),L(16),M(16),F(16)
   81 DIM P(16),Q(16),S(16),R(16),G(16)
   82 DIM V(3),T(3)
   85 FOR I=1 TO 16
   86 READ K(I)
   87 NEXT I
   88 REM K-M CALIBRATION DATA FOR YELL 29
   90 DATA 15.14,13.3,9.66,4.93,1.82,.52,.14,.09
   95 DATA 0.06,.05,.04,.04,.03,.03,.03
  100 FOR I= 1 TO 16
  102 READ L(I)
  103 REM K-M CALIBRATION DATA FOR RED 57
  104 NEXT I
  105 DATA 3,2.91,3.06,3.95,5.97,8.29,9.44,9.02
  110 DATA 6.97,2.97,.87,.23,.87,.54,.43,.04
  120 FOR I=1 TO 16
  125 READ M(I)
  130 NEXT I
  132 REM K-M CALIBRATION DATA FOR BLUE 41
  135 DATA 3.09,2.03,1.1,.9
  137 DATA 1.19,1.82,2.83,4.42
  139 DATA 6.28,8.46,9.44,9.23
  140 DATA 9.02,6.50,3.23,1.29
  145 FOR I =1 TO 16
  147 READ G(I)
  148 NEXT I
  149 REM K/S DATA FOR SUBSTRATE
  150 DATA .53,.38,.27,.20
  152 DATA .15,.11,.09,.07
  153 DATA .06,.05,.04,.04
  154 DATA .04,.03,.03,.03
  160 FOR I=1 TO 16
  162 READ P(I)
  164 NEXT I
  165 REM 10 DEGREE D65 DATA FOR CIE X VALUE
  166 DATA 0.252,3.232,6.679,6.096
  168 DATA 1.721,0.059,2.184,6.810
  170 DATA 12.165,16.467,17.233,12.894
  172 DATA 6.226,2.111,0.573,0.120
  180 FOR I = 1 TO 16
  182 READ Q(I)
  184 NEXT I
  185 REM 10 DEGREE D65 DATA FOR CIE Y VALUE
  186 DATA 0.023,0.330,1.106,2.620
  188 DATA 4.938,8.668,13.846,17.355
  190 DATA 17.157,14.148,10.105,6.020
  192 DATA 2.587,0.827,0.222,0.047
  200 FOR I=1 TO 16
  202 READ S(I)
  204 NEXT I
  205 REM 10 DEGREE D65 DATA FOR CIE Z VALE
  206 DATA 1.090,15.383,34.376,35.355
  208 DATA 15.897,3.997,1.046,0.237
  210 DATA 0.002,-0.002,0.00,0.00
  212 DATA 0,0,0,0
  220 W=W+1
  230 FOR I = 1 TO 16
  240 F(I)=G(I)+K(I)*C1+L(I)*C2+M(I)*C3
  250 R(I)=1 +F(I) - SQR(F(I)*2+F(I)^2)
  255 NEXT I
  257 X=0
  258 Y=0
  259 Z=0
  260 FOR I = 1 TO 16
  270 X=X+P(I)*R(I)
  275 Y=Y+Q(I)*R(I)
  280 Z=Z+S(I)*R(I)
  290 NEXT I
  295 C1=INT(C1*1000+0.5)/1000
  297 C2=INT(C2*1000+0.5)/1000
  300 C3 =INT(C3*1000+0.5)/1000
  310 X=INT(X*10+0.5)/10
  312 Y=INT(Y*10+0.5)/10
  314 Z=INT(Z*10+0.5)/10
  320 PRINT "C1=";C1;TAB(9)"C2=";C2;TAB(18) "C3=";C3;
  322 PRINT TAB(27);X;TAB(32);Y;TAB(37);Z
  325 FOR I=1 TO 3
  330 FOR J=1 TO 3
  340 A(I,J)=0
  350 NEXT J
  360 NEXT I
  365 FOR I =1 TO 16
  370 E=(R(I)^2)*2/(R(I)^2-1)
  380 A(1,1)=A(1,1)+P(I)*E*K(I)
  385 A(1,2)=A(1,2)+P(I)*E*L(I)
  390 A(1,3)=A(1,3)+P(I)*E*M(I)
  395 A(2,1)=A(2,1)+Q(I)*E*K(I)
  400 A(2,2)=A(2,2)+Q(I)*E*L(I)
  410 A(2,3)=A(2,3)+Q(I)*E*M(I)
  420 A(3,1)=A(3,1)+S(I)*E*K(I)
  430 A(3,2)=A(3,2)+S(I)*E*L(I)
  440 A(3,3)=A(3,3)+S(I)*E*M(I)
  450 NEXT I
  500 B(1,1) =A(2,2)*A(3,3)-A(3,2)*A(2,3)
  510 B(1,2) = -A(2,1)*A(3,3)+A(3,1)*A(2,3)
  520 B(1,3) = A(2,1)*A(3,2)-A(3,1)*A(2,2)
  530 B(2,1)=-A(1,2)*A(3,3)+A(3,2)*A(1,3)
  540 B(2,2)=A(1,1)*A(3,3)-A(3,1)*A(1,3)
  550 B(2,3)=-A(1,1)*A(3,2)+A(3,1)*A(1,2)
  560 B(3,1)=A(1,2)*A(2,3)-A(2,2)*A(1,3)
  570 B(3,2)=-A(1,1)*A(2,3)+A(2,1)*A(1,3)
  580 B(3,3)=A(1,1)*A(2,2)-A(2,1)*A(1,2)
  590 D=A(1,1)*B(1,1)+A(1,2)*B(1,2)+A(1,3)*B(1,3)
  600 V(1)=X1-X
  610 V(2)=Y1-Y
  620 V(3)=Z1-Z
  650 FOR I=1 TO 3
  660 T(I)=0
  670 NEXT I
  680 FOR I= 1 TO 3
  690 FOR J=1 TO 3
  700 C(I,J)=B(J,I)/D
  710 T(I)=T(I)+C(I,J)*V(J)
  720 NEXT J
  730 NEXT I
  740 C1=C1+T(1)
  750 C2=C2+T(2)
  760 C3=C3+T(3)
  770 IF W<10 GOTO 220
  800 END
```

169